Amazing Optical Illusions

THIS IS A CARLTON BOOK

Text and artwork copyright © 2006 Archimedes' Laboratory™
Design copyright © 2006 Carlton Books Ltd

First published in 2006 by Carlton Books Limited
20 Mortimer Street
London W1T 3JW

A CIP catalogue record for this book is available from the
British Library

Editorial Manager: Roland Hall
Art Direction: Clare Baggaley
Design: Luke Griffin
Production: Claire Hayward

ISBN: 978-1-86200-975-2

Printed in Dubai

DEDICATION

To my hardy, timeless art professor, Felix Maurice, who taught
me a lot on the illusion of art and on my unlimited ego... and
whose name still puzzles me: is Felix the first or the last name?
– Gianni A. Sarcone

Page 3: Broken Plate?
If you concentrate on one of the lobster's eyes, after some time
(10–15 seconds) it will seem that the broken piece of plate
rejoins the rest. This amusing effect occurs because our brain
tends to subconsciously 'iron' out broken or sawn lines.

Amazing Optical Illusions

Over 150 illustrations

Gianni A. Sarcone & Marie-Jo Waeber

SEVENOAKS

Contents

"...And **God SAW** every thing that he had made, and, behold, it was very good."

- The *Holy Bible*, Gen. 1:1-30—2:1

INTRODUCTION

Vision is allusion

Since ancient times, humans have known that immediate perception is not a reading of physical reality. This is specifically illustrated by Plato's allegory of the cave: humans are likened to prisoners chained in a cave, unable to turn their heads and thus to see any real objects. All they can see are shadows of objects projected by a light source on the wall of the cave. What the prisoners perceive, therefore, are just shadows and echoes cast by objects that they do not see at all. Such prisoners would mistake appearance (shadows) for reality.

But what is seeing? What is vision? What is the visual experience? Vision is the most creative act that a human being is capable of. Seeing is depicting the world on the living canvas of our mind. As we depict well only what we really know, our mind is both the canvas and the artist. In this creative process, the eyes represent nothing other than a medium with which our mind interprets and 'reconstructs' the reality around us. The poet Novalis said: "the eyes are a 'superficial' organ". In fact, we will never perceive the real world because it is strongly dependent of our body and our mind. Yes, vision isn't quite the 100 per cent natural process that folk may think... It relies for a large part on *learned skills* that are helpful in interpreting our near environment, but can sometimes deceive. That's why the study of visual illusions and mental fallacies is important: they reveal the magic and the limits of our perception (or consciousness). Some illusions teach us to doubt and to question the many appearances of the reality – they are a kind of school for life.

When you look in the mirror, the person in front of you, even though you are used to the image, isn't really you. It is an alien with the heart on the right and the liver on the left. How much imagination do we need to understand how we truly perceive ourselves and how others perceive us? Try this experiment: scan a photo of yourself and, with the help of a photo retouching software, flip it horizontally to create a mirror image and print it. Now compare this image with the original photo. Which of the two faces do you prefer? Show both images to a friend, and ask which version he or she prefers. You will probably prefer the mirror image and your friend the 'normal' version. It's a question of habit – we prefer that which we are used to... Two visions of the same person! But the illusion is also of the mind; especially when we believe we can control our thoughts. Try NOT thinking of a polar bear. Did you manage it, or did the polar bear lumber slowly into your mind? Now try to think of a green, green man and think quickly of a number from 1 to 5... Then a number from 5 to 10. We bet you thought of 3 and 7? Another example is when imagination and will 'collide' – it is always imagination which leads the way. It is easy to walk across a board laid flat on the ground but, with all the will in the world, quite impossible to walk the same plank suspended between two buildings ten floors up. The consciousness is one of the greatest mysteries of the brain. Many actions – walking, catching the bus, answering the phone – are performed unconsciously and we only become aware of them after they are completed. A recent study has revealed that our

Just Gray...

Color experiment with gray lines... What happens is called color assimilation: the gray color appears bluish in contact with blue, and orange-colored in contact with orange, giving the impression of a color gradation.

conscious decision to move a limb is done more or less one second after the area of the brain has activated this movement. Therefore, is it ourselves who control our own behavior, or is free will only an illusion created by our brains? Illusions, always illusions... We are immersed in a sea of mental illusions: illusions of certainty, illusions of security...

What actually are optical or visual illusions? In the fewest words, they are particular illusions that deceive the human visual system into perceiving something that is not present or incorrectly perceiving what is present. Optical illusions can be categorized as: **physical illusions**, **physiological illusions** and **cognitive illusions**. Physical illusions are phenomenal illusions that occur before light enters the eye, such as a mirage, a rainbow or a straw in a glass of water. Physiological illusions are the effects on the eyes or brain of prolonged stimulation of a specific type: brightness, tilt, color, movement... Cognitive illusions interact with different levels of perceptual processing, and in-built assumptions or 'knowledge' are misdirected. Cognitive illusions are commonly divided into ambiguous illusions, distorting illusions, and paradoxical illusions.

Optical illusions have been studied for millennia. Even our prehistoric ancestors may have been puzzled by visual illusions, although they didn't leave traces of it... They must surely have noticed and experienced some visual phenomena, such as:

– the after-image effect on their eyes, when looking into the sun;

– a stick that seems broken when half of it is put in water;

– the Moon illusion (the rising Moon seems twice as large as the Moon in the zenith);

– and the natural optical phenomenon called a mirage.

The ancient Greeks used a technique known as *entasis* which incorporates a slight convexity in the columns of a temple to compensate for the illusion of concavity created by parallel lines (more recently, Rolls-Royce cars all made use of entasis in their radiator grills).

Over the years, many people have found uses for optical illusions. We could say that tricking people's eyes has been a way of life in art, technology and in entertainment. But why do most people like optical illusions? Perhaps because illusions look like magic or conjuring? Rod Serling once wrote: "In any quest for magic, in any search for sorcery, witchery, legerdemain, first check the human heart" (*Dust*). Each one of us has his own reasons for appreciating being surprised or puzzled by visual illusions: some, with a scientific instinct, love searching for the reasoning and logical explanation behind them (thinking they are smart enough to figure it out!). Some, with an artistic background, are rather attracted by the aesthetics, and others by the contemplative aspect of the illusions. It is known that people who like to be fooled by optical illusions are 'big kids'. Our opinion is that the marvel of optical illusions takes us back to the dawn of our childhood, that nostalgia that haunts every one of us.

To resume, optical illusions teach us how we perceive things – they show us the seams in the fabric of the reality we

Tight Position
Are you really looking at this man reading from behind? This is a kind of undecidable figure. The lower and upper part of the man seem to have different directions.

(re)create. In this book, divided into seven main topics (ambiguous figures, impossible figures, hidden figures, color perception, moving patterns, paradoxes and magic), you will find an interesting and suggestive collection of visual puzzles to solve and optical illusions to explore, enjoy and experiment with. A large part of the illusions were invented and designed by the authors, while some others are adaptations of lesser known optical illusions or based on recent studies made by leading researchers in the field of the cognitive neurosciences, such as E. Andelson, H. Ashida, J. Faubert, G. Kanisza, A. Kitaoka, A. Logvinenko, B. Pinna and H. Van Tuijl. To complete the picture, you will find at the end of this book a catalog of historical optical illusions discovered by scientists, psychologists and artists of the nineteenth and twentieth centuries.

Each illusion, when necessary, is explained with simple and clear words – this book is intended for everyone – but please be aware that most of the explanations are empirical and based on intuitions rather than on real scientific proof. Some perceptive illusions are still under discussion and the scientists who studied these phenomena are only able to make suppositions. We have also to say that researchers sometimes have the bad habit of concealing their ignorance and build from the slightest little thing great short-lived theories that are not always consistent nor founded (who remembers the clumsy theory of right and left brain?). The best way to understand how and why an illusion works is to experience it with your friends and try constructing a variant... If the variant works, that means that you have understood the secret mechanism of the illusion. We hope that you will use our stunning illustrations as a resource and inspiration for designing and creating new optical illusions.

In conclusion, dear Reader, all the world is a stage, but there is always an unexpected curtain to rise. Enjoy!

Gianni A. Sarcone
Marie-Jo Waeber

Gianni A. Sarcone and Marie-Jo Waeber are the authors of columns and articles for newspapers and magazines featuring visual puzzles and math brainteasers. They have written and published several educational text books and illustrated books, in English, French and Italian, on puzzles and on the mechanism of vision. They are co-founders of Archimedes' Laboratory™, a consulting network of experts specializing in improving and developing creativity.

Perspective, geometric and angle illusions

Our brain often translates the physical image we perceive into an image which is more useful to our senses. As you experience it in everyday life, there is a distinction between the *actual size* of an object, its *apparent* or *angular size* and its *imaginary size*. The actual size of an object cannot be observed, because in order for our eyes to focus upon that object it must be at a certain distance. But you can calculate or measure it. The perceived or angular size of an object is a measure of

A

B

Brighten It Up
The colors of the rainbow in figure A are faded. To restore their intensity, stare at the white dot in figure B for 20–30 seconds, then shift your gaze back to figure A. This effect is based on color adaptation.

how large the object actually 'appears' to be and depends primarily on the *visual angle* subtended by the object on the retina in our eyes. All other things being equal, the object that subtends the larger visual angle will appear larger. The visual angle is dependent on the actual size of the object and on the distance the object is from our eyes. A camel may not pass through the eye of a needle, but its image – apparent size – can! Actually, it would be possible to see an 80-inch wide camel placed at a distance of 0.6 miles from you, through a two millimeter-wide eye of a needle. What about the imaginary size? Psychologically, we tend sometimes to see objects larger (or smaller) than they appear in reality. For example, it's very difficult to determine at a rough guess the real size of circular objects.

The fact that we have two eyes (binocular vision) is more than sufficient to provide information on distances, and for that reason we don't need three... One of these binocular distance cues is called *convergence*. Convergence refers to the turning in of our eyes as objects come closer to them (and is what causes you to have a squint!). The other thing that happens as objects come closer is that our visual accommodation changes.

Another cue to distance perception, especially for more complex scenes in which there are multiple objects, is *binocular disparity*. That means that each eye records a different angle of the visual field. Yet another cue to distance is *motion parallax*. As you move from one location to another objects at various distances will move in a direction dependent on where you are fixating. Finally, it turns out

that color and brightness can also have an effect on how far away something appears.

Another factor affecting perceived size is *size constancy*. This phenomenon results in objects of known size tending to appear constant in size regardless of their actual distance. So, for example, if you are looking at your friend and that friend starts walking away from you, the friend does not, at the same time, start to appear smaller, even though the visual angle subtended by that friend is getting less and less. Well, size constancy also depends on the distance and if it is large enough, known objects will appear smaller. If you have ever looked at the ground from a very tall building, you will have noticed that people on the sidewalks and cars in the streets look very small. *Perspective* also plays a part in perception of size.

In conclusion, despite our ability to judge distance and size differences in many cases, our ability is distorted by a wide range of subjective factors. What is really interesting is that size illusions affect only the visual perception, and not the senses which control our organs of motion. Thus, scientists presume that there are two kinds of visual connections – one directly concerning visual perception and the other involving motory control.

In the following pages we will explore some of the things that affect our ability to estimate comparative lengths, sizes and shapes, and examine some geometrical properties that induce those deformations. But what are the main errors in size perception? First, we tend to perceive any line or segment enclosed

Quick Color Eyesight Test
Close one eye and stare at the two colored squares each containing the letter E. If one of the Es seems darker you may need a pair of glasses! Do the test with the other eye too. This test is based on the chromatic aberration of the lens in our eye making red colors focus slightly behind the retina and green colors, slightly in front. In normal conditions chromatic aberration passes unnoticed, but a slight nearsightedness or farsightedness increases the irregularity, making a color go over the edges of a letter E.

He took my glasses off and he said, "Without your glasses, why, you're beautiful!" I said, "Without my glasses, you're not half bad either."

- Kit Hollerbach

between two acute angles (less than 90 degrees) as shorter than it really is, and a segment enclosed between two obtuse angles (more than 90 degrees) as longer. The second most frequent error is that parallel lines seem closer to each other when they are oblique rather than displayed orthogonally. We will also take into consideration the so-called *alignment illusions* and perceptive distortions, whereby repeating regular background patterns can so strongly dominate other regular geometric shapes placed on to them, that they appear distorted.

Color perception

As the neurologist Sir John Eccles clarified once and for all: color doesn't exist at all in nature! Color only starts to exist when our perception systems produce the impression of 'color': light is perceived on the retina as a stimulus and is processed into a perception of color in our brain. In substance, colors are already illusions in themselves.

That's why color sensibility is individual and color taste differs from man to woman and even from country to country (different cultures have different terms for colors, and may also assign some color names to slightly different parts of the spectrum). Those variations in color sensibility between man and woman may have been especially important in very early times, when humans were hunter-gatherers. Enhanced color perception would have allowed women, who were traditionally gatherers, to better discriminate among colored fruits, insects and background foliage.

Yes, we don't all have the same sensibility towards colors... Some people can't distinguish certain hues or colors at all. This is a problem of 'color deficiency' (commonly known as 'color blindness') and is most commonly due to an inherited condition. Color deficiency seems to occur in about 10 per cent of males of European origin and about one-half of 1 per cent of females. Red/green color deficiency is by far the most common form and causes problems in distinguishing reds and greens. Another color deficiency, blue/yellow, also exists but is rare, and there is no available test for it. Total color deficiency (seeing only in shades of gray) is extremely rare. There is no treatment for color deficiency, nor is it usually the cause of any significant disability. However, it can be very frustrating for individuals affected by it. General assessment of color vision can be made with the Ishihara card test.

Color serves a special function in the processes of vision. Our ability to analyze and process colors is a result of having three types of cone receptors in the retina, which have different light wavelength sensitivities: the short (blue), the mid (green) and the long-wavelength (red) cone receptors. But seeing a color involves making comparisons, because all that a single cone receptor can do is capture light and analyze its intensity... it tells nothing about color! Because of the overlap between the sensitivity ranges, it is not possible to stimulate ONLY the mid-wavelength (green) cone receptors: the other cones must be stimulated to some degree at the same time. To see any color, our brain must compare the input from the other cone receptors and then

> ## "I want you to realize that there exists no color in the natural world, and no sound, nothing of this kind; no textures, no patterns, no beauty, no scent..."
>
> - Sir John Eccles

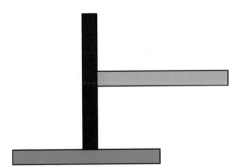

Yellow Rod = Green Rod?
These rods form the Chinese character 'high'. Are the yellow and green rods of the same length? They are – measure them!

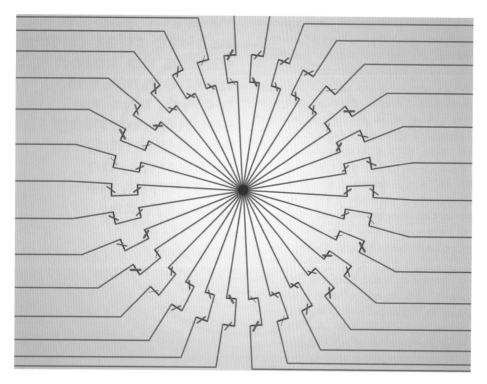

Follow My Eyes

Stare at the center of the geometric picture shown here. Keeping your gaze fixed on the central blue spot, move your head backwards and forwards several times. What happens? The blue concentric circles appear to rotate in opposite directions!

Photocopy the picture and paste it on a rectangular piece of cardboard. Then, keeping the image 30cm away from your eyes, give a swinging movement. What do you see now? The concentric circles seem to expand or shrink, like the aperture of a camera, depending on the swinging direction you give to the image.

make many other comparisons as well.

So, on your PC screen, blue, green and red lights are sufficient to create the impression of color. But is it possible to create the illusion of color using only two different single-color lights? Edwin Herbert Land, the inventor of the 'Polaroid', demonstrated that we can perceive nearly the full range of colors by viewing superimposed two monochrome slides: one illuminated with red light and the other with white light. Land's experiment confirms that the color sensibility of a particular category of cone receptors is relative and depends on the other cone categories. Land also demonstrated in another experiment, using colored patches, the *color constancy*, i.e. our

tendency to see an object as a certain color, no matter what color the object might be. For example, if we have an expectation to see an apple as red, we will see – or have the impression to see – a red apple, even if it's too dark for us to tell what color it really is. According to Land, the eye and the brain (the retina and cortex) form a single optical system ('retinex') – so, apparently, our past prejudice literally 'colors' our world.

Certainly, the eye is not a perfect optical instrument due to possible chromatic aberration of the lens, yellowing with age, and variations of sensitivity. But coupled with the brain, human vision is satisfactorily reliable and constant. Here, we've listed some effects created by our brain that condition our way to see the world around us.

Color adaptation or assimilation is the tendency of the eye to adapt in seconds to most prevailing light sources. Because of this effect, the eye can, in turn, accurately identify the colors of objects under changing lighting conditions. Adaptation will be seen by a person traveling in a vehicle with tinted windows; if, for instance, the tint is blue, the landscape will at first seem suffused with a blue cast but, as the eye quickly desensitizes itself to blue, the view will soon reassume its normal coloration.

Lightness constancy – Objects that are viewed under different lighting conditions usually 'look' the same to us. For example, a white T-shirt will look the same whether it is brightly lit on a sunny day or dimly lit on an overcast day. This is despite the fact that the wavelength of light that reaches the retinas in each case is different. This is explained by the fact that the brightness of an object's surroundings usually changes in proportion to the change in brightness of the object itself.

After-image is a negative or complementary 'ghost' of a color seen after prolonged stimulation of the eye. An after-image occurs by staring first at a black spot on a white surface for around 20 seconds, then shifting one's gaze to a black surface; a floating white spot will be seen briefly. The after-image of a red spot would be blue-green, that of a blue one would be yellow-orange, and that of a violet spot would be greenish yellow. After-image effects involve the optical nerves. An optical nerve is composed of millions of neuronal fibers which connect the retina to the brain by decoding the stimuli of the retina into three different signals: light difference (black/white) or luminance, red/green color difference, and blue/yellow color difference. When you stare at a red square for 20 seconds or more, the cells of the optical nerve which transmit the **presence of red AND the absence of green** will be under tension and will be saturated; consequently, when the stimulus suddenly disappears, the brain will interpret this stimulus cut effectively as the **absence of red AND the presence of green**. A green square will therefore appear in your visual field... It's like a short flip-flop effect. Interestingly, most standards for television transmission use a very similar decoding system, with one luminance and two chrominance channels.

A curious effect called *retinal rivalry* may be obtained by stimulating both retinas, each with a different color. For instance, when blue glass is placed before one eye and yellow or red before the other, the two independent monocular fields fight for supremacy; vision appears alternately in one color and then the other, and the brain has great trouble resolving the images.

Simultaneous color contrast is an effect in which the contrast between adjacent colors is enhanced by the eye. The effect is particularly strong with a pair of complementary colors, such as red and green or orange and blue. If these colors are put together in tight patterns, the resulting contrast is so strong that flicker will occur and the eye may experience considerable discomfort. *Simultaneous lightness contrast* is an effect in which a

Continuous Lines?
Are the oblique lines in the square continuous from side to side? No, but you have to take a closer look at the pattern in order to realize it.

Grey Sofa
Is the gray zone in A darker than the gray zone in B? The gray zones in A and B have exactly the same hue. We tend to perceive the gray zone in A to be darker. This experiment shows that the perceived brightness doesn't rely only on the amount of light that reaches the eye from the observed object.

color of given brightness will look darker on a light background and brighter on a dark background. Simultaneous contrasts depend on *lateral inhibition* of our visual system.

Some photoreceptors of the retina are activated when they detect light, while others are activated in the absence of light. These two types usually encircle each other and are spread throughout the retina, creating receptive fields. Often, light can fall onto both light and dark photoreceptors, causing the two regions to compete with one another. One part of the receptive field wants to become active while the other part does not. This competitive interaction is called *lateral inhibition*. Because of this antagonistic nature of receptive fields, perceptual illusions, such as the Herman or Lingelbach grid illusion, can occur or when we look at certain patterns containing contrasting colors.

Since warm (reddish) colors tend to advance in our visual field and cold (bluish) colors tend to recede, objects painted in red and orange will seem to be slightly larger than those painted in cool blues and greens. Red cars or buses may

seem larger than they actually are, but a room painted in red will seem more confined than a blue one. The reason for these effects is *chromatic aberration*, a problem associated with lenses (including the one used to focus light in the human eye), in which light is refracted by different amounts according to its wavelength. As a result, yellow is the only color perfectly focused by the normal eye, with red focused slightly behind the retina and blue slightly in front. The second reason may be that associative elements come into play. For example, blue may seem to recede because of the association it has in our memory with distance (the sky, sea, distant mountains...). The value (relative lightness or darkness) of a color also affects our perception of the weight of an object.

In the following pages you will experience some effects related to color including: color and lightness illusions, neon color spreading effect, scintillating grid effect, Kanisza illusion, Boynton filling-in phenomenon...

Anomalous motion illusions
How is it possible to create the illusion of

"What is mind but motion in the intellectual sphere?"
- Oscar Wilde

motion with geometric and static images? There is a branch of modern art named *Op'art* (short for 'Optic art') which is concerned with such optic effects. Op'art paintings often play with optic interference and moiré to create illusory colors and motion. The precursor of the Op'art was Victor Vasarely, an Hungarian artist. But Bridget Riley is perhaps the best known of the op'artists. Taking Vasarely's lead, she painted a number of works consisting only of black and white lines. Riley's paintings depict an unreal geometric world which frequently give the impression of movement or color.

Anomalous or apparent motion illusions are based on alternating optical contrasts (clear/dark, vertical/horizontal, left/right) to create a perturbation, like a visual overload perturbing the retinal circuits, which can, among other things, make our eyesight flicker. There have been a number of analyses of the apparent motion illusion. The most obvious interpretation would seem to be in terms of what computer vision scientists call 'optic flow'. Until now, we can count roughly four different families of relative movement or kinetic effects:

- phantom movements, like moving flows, scintillating and popping-up patterns;
- floating images (such as Ouchi illusion);
- rotating shapes (B. Pinna and G. Brelstaff illusion);
- self-moving and spontaneous rotating shapes (peripheral drift illusion).

Let's go deeper into two of them...

PINNA ROTATING ILLUSION

The Pinna-Brelstaff rotating illusion consists of two (or more) concentric rings of slanted lines or geometric shapes. When an observer moves towards the display the two rings of geometric patterns appear to counter-rotate. The illusion is optimal when there is a 66 degree orientation difference between elements composing the inner and outer rings. This illusion can be nulled by introducing a physical rotation opposite to the direction of the illusory motion. In other words, geometric patterns that are actually counter-rotating are perceived as stationary. Three factors may cause this illusion: the luminance profile, the angular direction of the shapes and the bad integration of motion signals in our brain.

THE PERIPHERAL DRIFT ILLUSION

This illusion was first described by the scientists A. Fraser and K. Wilcox, and by J. Faubert. The most famous peripheral drift illusion, designed by A. Kitaoka, is called *Rotating Snakes*. It consists of concentric repeating patterns of white, yellow, black and blue, that evoke a striking illusion of motion. What makes this illusion so interesting is the fact that you are experiencing movement in the periphery, although you realize that the moving objects are not moving at all! We've discovered that if we retouch the *Rotating Snakes* image using the 'threshold application' of Photoshop, it reveals the image's darkest point and the illustration then shows radial patterns of optic flows.

While peripheral vision demonstrates movement over the entire field of the display, focusing on one particular part of the illusion shows that it is stationary. There are no definite answers to explain this phenomenon but the main characteristics of the illusion are:

1. Illusory motion appears in the direction from a black region to the adjacent dark-gray region or in the direction from a white region to the adjacent light-gray region.

Colors indicating the directions of illusory motion: black to dark-gray or white to light-gray.

2. It occurs well in peripheral vision. The object we fixate appears to be stationary.

3. It occurs well with stimuli of edges. Stimuli of smooth luminance profiles give weak illusions.

4. It occurs well with fragmented or curved edges. Stimuli made up of long edges give weak illusions.

5. It may be generated by involuntary halting eye movements.

Some illusory moving patterns work better on a computer screen (because of the luminance), so you can try scanning them and watching them on your PC.

Ambiguous, bistable and completion figures

Does the mind represent the world accurately and unambiguously? Actually, ALL inputs to the brain are, to some degree or another, 'ambiguous', allowing multiple interpretations. That's the reason why we have poets, artists, singers... The capacity to perceive and give different meanings to our environment is part of our human condition.

What are *ambiguous figures*? Briefly, ambiguous figures are 'two pictures in one' – looked at one way, we see one thing (e.g. a vase), but looked at in another way, we may see something else (e.g. two

faces in profile). They are somewhat similar to *bistable figures*, in that there are two ways to interpret each one, but bistable figures don't contain different subjects; they contain just one subject that flips perspective (e.g. Necker's cube).

One of the most antique ambiguous images, representing two confronted boars' heads that also form a facing panther head, was coined on early Lesbos money (Greece) about 2,500 years ago.

Ambiguous figures have long fascinated artists, children and others who enjoy surprises. The most famous example of ambiguity in painting is the *Mona Lisa*'s smile by Leonardo Da Vinci. In his book, *The Story of Art*, Ernest Gombrich reports: "Even in photographs of the painting we experience this strange effect, but in front of the original in the Paris Louvre it is almost uncanny. Sometimes she seems to mock at us, and then again we seem to catch something like sadness in her smile." Ambiguous figures, aka *equivocal images* or *metamorphic images*, are of special interest in the investigation of thinking. This is because they exemplify the fact that sometimes the same perceptual input can lead to very different representations, suggesting that the brain is actively involved in interpreting what we see rather than passively recording it. The curious aspect of ambiguous figures is that once you have perceived both figures, it is impossible to focus on only one without the other popping into your vision from time to time. Our brain, in fact, resolves visual ambiguity by means of oscillation.

Ambiguous figures include *figure-ground illusions*, *ambigrams* and what we will call *completion figures*. Figure-ground illusions

"A girl phoned me the other day and said 'come over, there's nobody home'. I went over. Nobody was home."

- Rodney Dangerfield

Early ambiguous images
Grecian coins circa 550–500B.C.

Temple of Colors

Examine the pale purple rectangles on the Greek temple. Are they of the same shade or do some rectangles appear darker than others? They are, in fact, all the same hue. Objects tend to be darker when placed on a clear luminous background and vice versa.

are illusions that swap around the main figure and its background. Ambigrams are graphic words or sentences that can be read in more than one way. Completion figures are patterns which the mind rather unambiguously interprets in a particular way despite the fact that the input is incomplete in relation to what is typically 'perceived'.

A certain style of completion figures, called *droodles*, was used in the late 50s to entertain puzzle enthusiasts and magazine readers. These cartoons were rather abstract line drawings accompanied by an implicit question: "What is it?" A punchline (usually

a funny description) finally made the cartoons obvious. Completion figures and droodles are based on the **pareidolia** (payr-eye-DOH-lee-uh), an innate human tendency to impose a pattern on random or ambiguous shapes. Astronomer Carl Sagan claimed that this tendency to see faces in tortillas, clouds, cinnamon buns and the like is an evolutionary trait. He writes: "*As soon as the infant can see, he recognizes faces, and we now know that this skill is hardwired in our brains. Those infants who a million years ago were unable to recognize a face, smiled back less, were less likely to win the hearts of their parents, and less likely to prosper.*

These days, nearly every infant is quick to identify a human face and to respond with a goony grin." (Sagan, 1995.)

Giving meaning to abstract forms can also be a way to exercise our visual thinking skills. Even Da Vinci heartily recommended this method of invention as a practical technique for "*opening the mind and putting it upon the scent of new thoughts*". He once wrote: "*If you look upon an old wall covered with dirt or the odd appearance of some streaked stones, you may discover several things like landscapes, battles, clouds, uncommon attitudes, humorous faces, draperies...*".

Impossible figures

Impossible figures are a development of the 'simpler' ambiguous figures. When we observe a two-dimensional picture on paper, we often interpret it as a three-dimensional figure. This insistence to view objects as three-dimensional can lead to interesting perceptual problems.

An *impossible object,* also called an *undecidable figure*, is an object that cannot exist according to the known laws of physics but has a description or representation suggesting, at first sight, that it can be constructed. Generally, impossible objects depend on the ambiguous connectivity possible in line drawings. We like to call these improbable objects *Frankenstein figures* because they are made by matching together two or more different points of view of the same object, or by extending and blending together the perspective of one object with another one. Some impossible figures are not immediately obvious. You have to focus your attention on a particular zone of the representation of the object – the line of fusion of the contrasting perspectives – to understand that it cannot be realized. The paradox is that if you consider a sufficiently small zone of the drawing, the oddness disappears. That is to say, the 'impossibility' is not here, or there – it is something about the object **as a whole**. This paradox could perfectly illustrate the philosophical principle which says that "the whole is something completely different than the sum of its parts"...

The more normal the impossible object looks, the more fascinating it becomes! Impossible figures aren't created to baffle your eyes – their structure should appear coherent and logic – they are designed to confuse your mind. The 'undecidability' of these figures invariably rests on them being interpreted as two-dimensional projections of what would be an impossible higher-dimensional object. Artist Maurice Escher is notable for many drawings that feature undecidable figures, sometimes the entire drawing being an impossible figure. Oscar Reutersvärd, another important artist, has conducted a lifelong exploration into the world of impossible figures, producing a prodigious body of work during his long career. Notable modern undecidable figures include:

- Impossible cube;
- Penrose stairs;
- Penrose triangle;
- Blivet (or devil's pitchfork).

We should not forget to add Mickey Mouse ears to the list. Yes, his ears do not follow the basic rules of perspective.

"What if everything is an illusion and nothing exists? In that case, I definitely overpaid for my carpet."

- Woody Allen

Children and adults alike are so accustomed to the current aspect of this cartoon character that they don't notice that his ears are actually impossible figures!

But impossible figures have a long history... In 1025, an unknown European artist unintentionally drew the first example of impossible figure art (three impossible pillars), in a painting *Madonna a Gyermekkel* ('Madonna and Child – Adoration of the Magi'). Another example of an impossible artistic object (a gallows!), was painted by Pieter Brueghel in *Magpie on the Gallows* (1568). However, the first artist who 'deliberately' misuses perspective to create an absurd and impossible landscape is the famous English artist William Hogarth (1697-1764), whose artwork *Perspective absurdities* formed the frontispiece to J. J. Kirby's book *Dr Brook Taylor's Method of Perspective Made Easy in Both Theory and Practice* (1754). This book was intended to teach people how to draw in perspective, so the caption asserted: "Whoever makes a design without the knowledge of perspective will be liable to such absurdities as are shown in this frontispiece".

Paradoxes: verbal illusions and vanish puzzles

Illusions and perceptive puzzles based on misconceptions and misperception can be useful to interest people in exploring and following logic and mathematical topics. On the following pages, you'll be able to experience the persuasive powers of the images and learn how a picture can sidetrack your senses of reasoning! We will also take the opportunity to deal with self-referential images and graphic words.

What exactly are *vanish puzzles*? Vanish puzzles (we've renamed them 'stereophanic puzzles') have existed for five centuries... but they still continue to amaze everyone! They can be of two types: figurative vanish puzzles and geometric vanish puzzles. Figurative vanish puzzles involve the rearranging of parts of a puzzle representing a scene with a series of elements (persons, animals, etc), so that, once the rearrangement is completed, an element of the scene disappears (or re-appears). Geometric vanish puzzles involve either the apparent disappearance of a part of their surface or an apparent reducing of their area when the pieces of the puzzles are re-arranged. The first example of vanishing area puzzles was discovered in the book *Libro d'Architettura Primo* by Sebastiano Serlio, an Italian architect of the Renaissance, even though Serlio didn't notice that any area had actually vanished. The first description and explanation of this paradox was found in a math puzzle book with a very long title: *Rational Recreations in which the Principles of Numbers and Natural Philosophy are Clearly & Copiously Elucidated, by a Series of Easy, Entertaining, Interesting Experiments among which are all those Commonly Performed with the Cards* (1774) by William Hooper.

Because of their visual impact, vanish puzzles are really striking, but their mechanism is quite simple: the part (figure, surface) which disappears is simply redistributed differently on the remaining parts of the puzzle; confirming Lavoisier's law which says "In nature, nothing is created, nothing is lost, all is transformed"... Then, the magic is only based on the **visual persuasion** that the puzzle is really different after

"I only shave men who do not shave themselves."

- Russel's paradox

manipulation. Well, vanish puzzles are just one aspect of perception puzzles... In this book, you will find some new games and magic tricks directly involving visual perception or visual memory.

A *self-reference* occurs when an object refers to itself. Reference is possible when there are two logical levels of interpretation which can sometimes interfere with each other (contradiction). The philosopher Heraclitus of Ephesus (*Herakleitos* in Greek) is recognized as one of the earliest philosophers who used self-reference in his dialectic, as in his statements:

– Nothing endures but change.
– Expect the unexpected.

The elliptical logic of his aphorisms earned Heraclitus the epithet 'Obscure'.

Many self-referential paradoxes are hidden in our everyday language ("there's something I want to tell you BEFORE I start talking..."). They are like optical illusions – they seem normal but when you examine them closely, the incongruity becomes obvious! Some self-referential statements can lead to paradoxes. The most famous self-referential paradox, called 'the Liar Paradox', is an argument that arrives at a contradiction by reasoning about a Liar Sentence. The classical Liar Sentence is the following:

– This sentence is false.

Actually, 'this sentence' is neither true or false... Experts in the field of philosophical logic have never agreed on the way out of the problem despite 2,300 years of attention...

"A table with a broken leg remains a table. But a table from which the four legs have been removed becomes only a flat piece of wood. At what moment did it cease to be a table?"

- Carlo Suares

Blinking and vanishing dots (left)
Shift your gaze around the blue circle and you may see the yellow dots blinking. Now, if you stare at one yellow dot for a while, the other dots vanish apart from the ones very close to the observed dot. This is a variant of the Herman's grid illusion. When the yellow dots are not in the central vision of the observer, they gradually disappear.

Gallery I

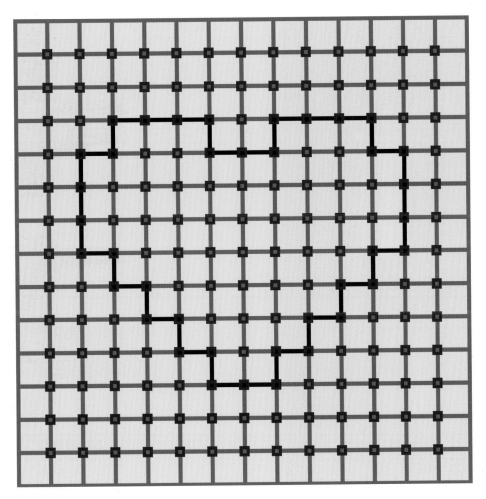

Neon Heart

Can you see an orange neon heart with a bright halo around it? View the picture from a good distance. The color in the background is perfectly uniform. The apparent orange color is created by the interaction of the black lines with the yellow background, and the apparent white halo by the interaction of the blue lines with the small dark squares.

Just Two Anomalies
There was a party, but where is the bottle?
Do you see another oddity?

Cloud Test
With just one stroke transform these clouds into a forest.

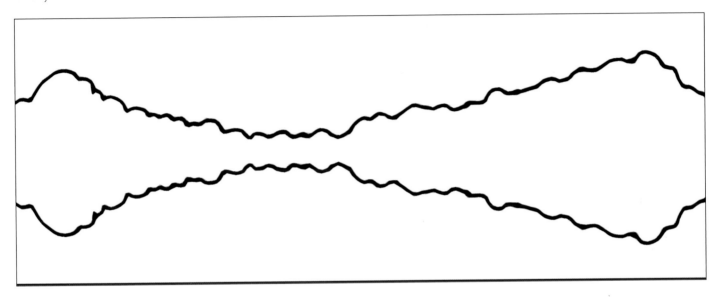

Greek Temple

Cut the puzzle (copy it first!) into two pieces
in order to make a column of the temple
vanish when the pieces are perfectly
rearranged. Impossible?

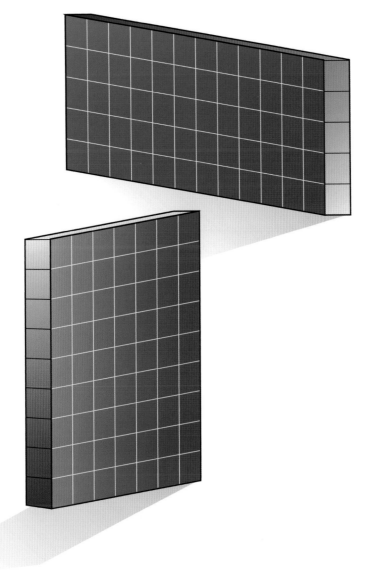

Low Walls

Are the blue surfaces of the low walls different? Can you calculate their area?

Visual Fitting Test

Which shape (A, B or C) fits exactly into the pentagonal hole?

A

B

C

Impossible Tearings
Take a strip of paper and make two
incisions in it as shown in the
picture. Hold the strip by its ends and pull
in order to break the strip.
What is the probability that the central
piece marked with an X falls
out: 1/3, 2/3 or 3/3?

Impossible Stairs

Arrows

Is the red arrow longer or shorter than the blue one?

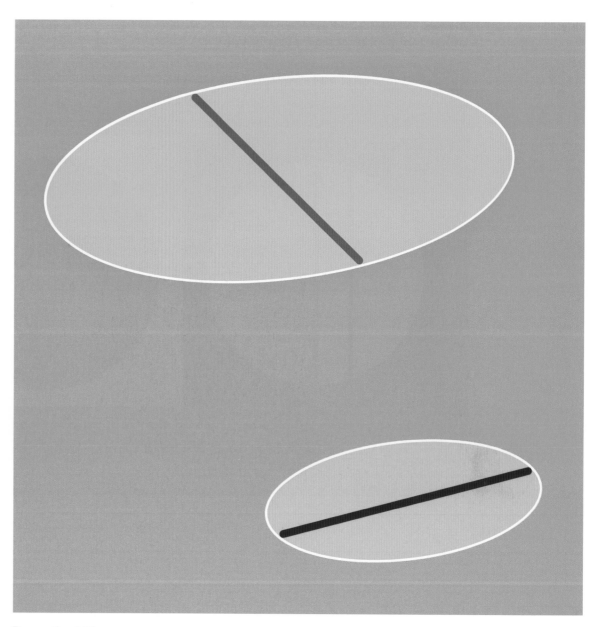

Deceptive Ellipses
Which line seems longer, the red one or the blue one?

Line A = Line B?
Are lines A and B really the same length?

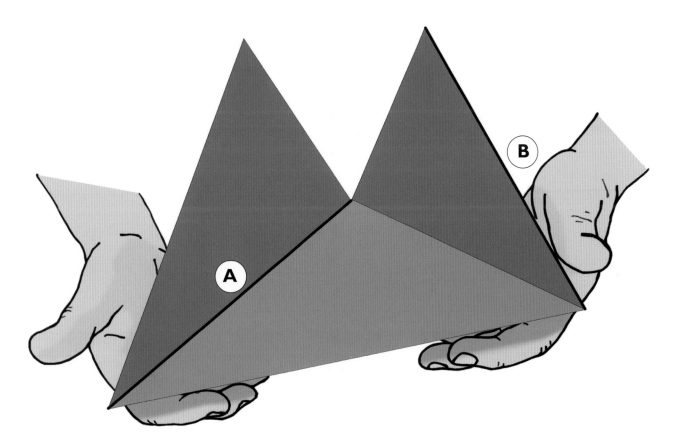

Curved Lines

Which arc segment has the greatest radius of curvature, A or B?

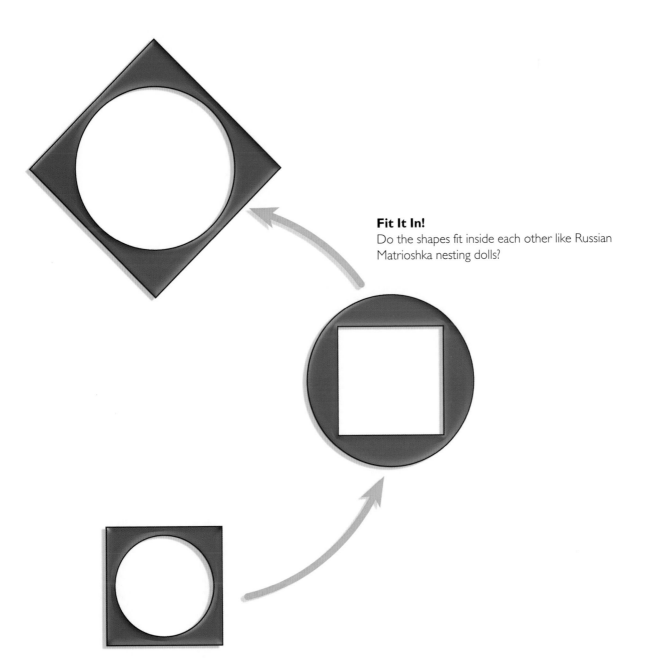

Fit It In!
Do the shapes fit inside each other like Russian Matrioshka nesting dolls?

Geometrical Visual Effects
Interesting geometrical effects with concentric squares.

A

B

Line A = Line B?
Are lines A and B the same length?

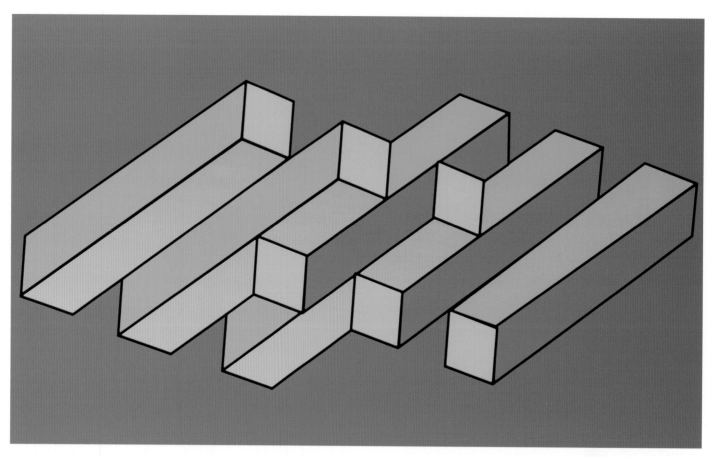

Impossible Rods

Which group of rods is on top in the picture and which one is underneath?

Vibrating I-Ching

In the picture are illustrated the 64 I-Ching symbols. These antique signs are part of Chinese philosophy. But they can also produce optical illusions. Do you see gray spots between the I-Ching symbols? Do you perceive some vertical flows? These effects are induced by lateral inhibition of our visual system.

Side A = Side B?

Which side seems shorter, side A or side B?

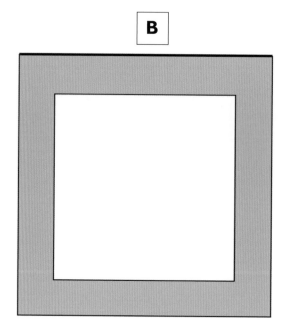

Line A = Line B?

Line B seems longer... but are you sure?

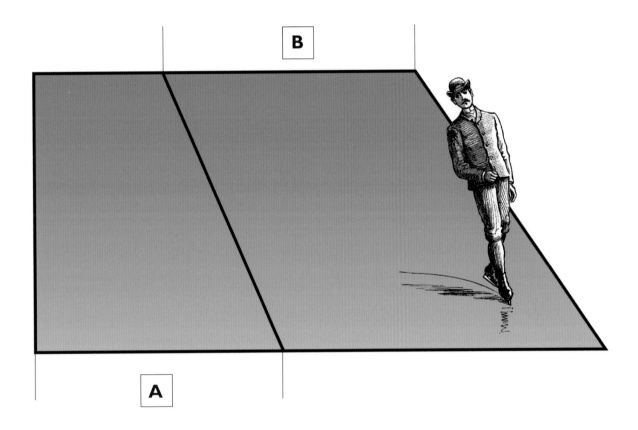

The upside-down
sentence is *TRUE*

si ǝɔuǝʇuǝs

umop - ǝpᴉsdn ǝɥꓕ

Visual Logic Paradox
This is either an ambigram (turn the page upside-down) or a
self-referential paradox. Now ponder whether the sentence is
true or false.

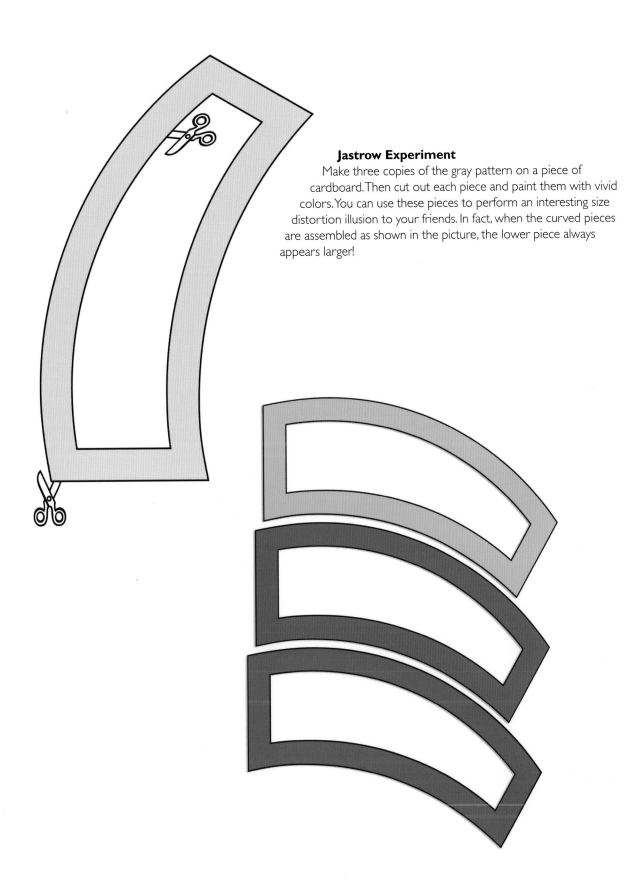

Jastrow Experiment

Make three copies of the gray pattern on a piece of cardboard. Then cut out each piece and paint them with vivid colors. You can use these pieces to perform an interesting size distortion illusion to your friends. In fact, when the curved pieces are assembled as shown in the picture, the lower piece always appears larger!

Gallery I Notes

Page 24

The bottle is concealed between the two glasses. The other oddity is that it is impossible to say if the candelabra has two or three sticks.

Page 25

Here is a forest reflected in a mountain lake.

Page 26

Page 27

Visually, the first wall seems to have an area of (12 x 5 =) 60 square units; and the second one, an area of (7 x 9 =) 63 square units. But actually, the blue surfaces are identical in shape and size, even though they look different! This illusion is related to the "crossing parallelogram" illusion. To find the real area of the blue surfaces, called parallelograms, you have to multiply their **base** by their **height**.

Page 28

Shape A!

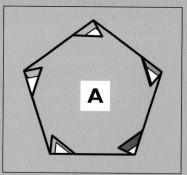

Page 29

The probability that the central piece marked with an X falls out is 0/3! This is the illustration of an improper use of probabilities for a physical event. We are simply deceived by our common sense.

Page 31

Red arrow = blue arrow!

Page 32

The blue line is longer than the red one. Measure them!

Page 33

Yes, they are.

Page 34

In fact, the arc segments are identical. The context in which the arc is placed determines its appearance.

Page 35

No. None can be fitted into another!

Page 37

Yes, they are the same length, despite the fact they look different. This is a variant of the Ponzo illusion.

Page 38

It is impossible to determine which group of rods is on top. These are just impossible figures.

Page 40

The hypotenuse, A, of the triangle seems shorter than side B of the square. However, they are the same length.

Page 41

In fact, line A = line B.

Page 42

This contradictory sentence is not resolvable in conventional logic systems. But not all self-referential sentences are paradoxical: consider 'this sentence is true'.

THE UPSIDE-DOWN SENTENCE IS TRUE
But if the upside-down sentence is true,
this sentence is false (contradiction);
Etc.......

THE UPSIDE-DOWN SENTENCE IS FALSE
But if the upside-down sentence is false,
this sentence is true (contradiction);
Etc.........

Gallery II

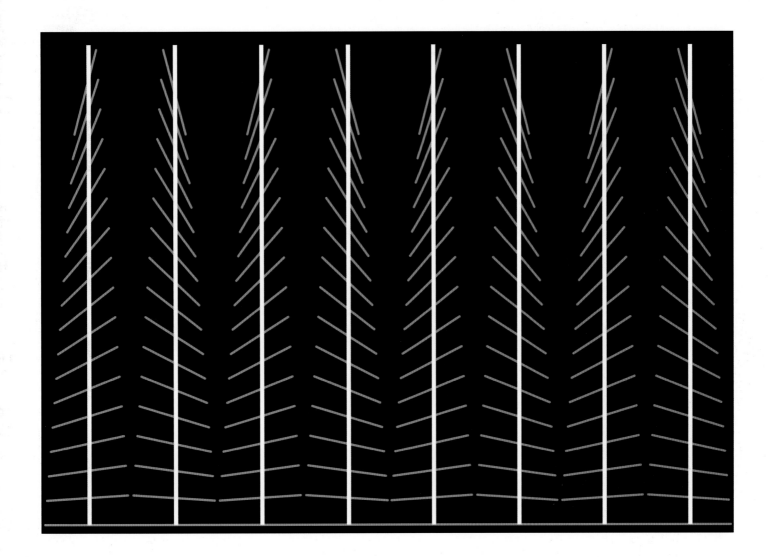

Distorted Lines

Do the lines tend to bend in at the top? No; it's just an illusion!

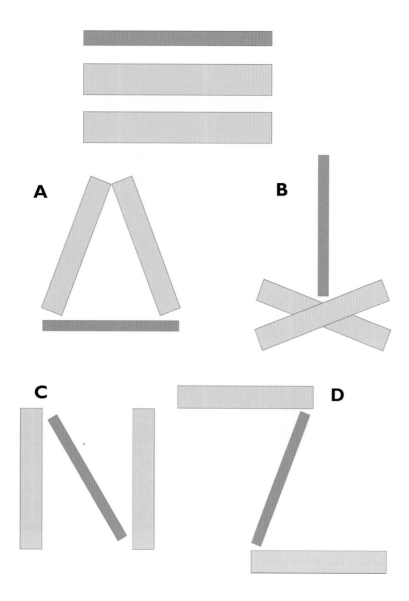

Paper Strips
Make two sets of three paper strips as shown in the picture and form, in turn, figures A and B. Strangely, in configuration A the thinner paper strip looks smaller than the thicker paper strips; in B the effect is reversed! Finally, make figures C and D; curiously, the paper strip in the middle looks longer in configuration D. Try this experiment with your friends...

Impossible Stairs 2

444444

888888

Fours and Eights

Consider the two rows of numbers.
Are all the fours the same thickness?
What about the eights?

A

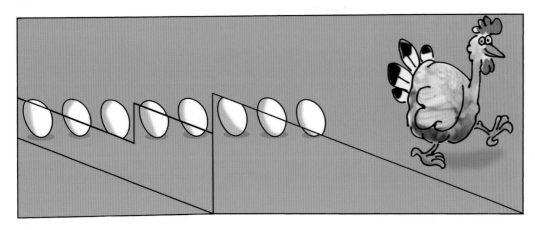

Befuddling Chicken and Eggs Puzzle

Which came first, the chicken or the egg? Well, the problem here is: who 'stole' the egg from Chiquita, our favorite chicken? As you can see in the four-piece puzzle in A, there are eight eggs…

Now, if we move some of the puzzle pieces around (B), an egg disappears along with a portion of the puzzle. But the missing portion doesn't have an egg on it!

How does this work?

B

Zöllner Revisited
The conjunction of parallel lines and sets of oblique strokes creates an interesting distortion illusion.

Tracing Star

First, photocopy the star. Then, take a pencil and trace a line within its borders while you are looking in the mirror at your drawing. You can hide the drawing with a book as shown in the picture. Find it easy?

Seal or...?

Can you see how to transform a marine mammal into a flying animal?

Solitude

Is the old lady really alone? How many people are with her?

Aligned?

Which line segments aren't aligned correctly to form a straight line, the magenta or the green ones?

Lines
Is the blue line longer than any of the red lines?

A

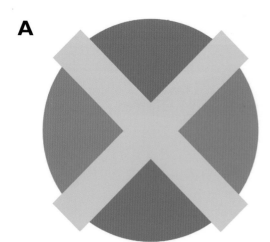

Sliced Colors

Consider both colored figures in A and B. In which case (A or B) are the vertical green slices the same shade as the horizontal slices?

B

Visual Memory Test

Concentrate on both red and green symbols for ten seconds. Relax...
Now select one of the playing cards – any of them – and firmly
concentrate on it. Memorize your card, then turn the page over!

Magic Cards
Believe it or not, the card you selected has been removed from the assortment and turned over. Right?

A

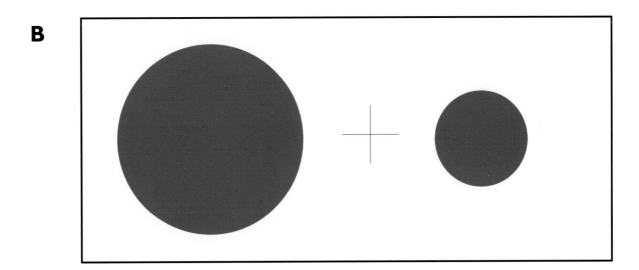

B

Bold the A
To enlarge one of the 'a' letters shown in diagram A, stare at the dots
in diagram B for about 20-30 seconds, then look at the letters
'a'. You should see a letter becoming larger and bolder!
(The experiment works better under bright light).

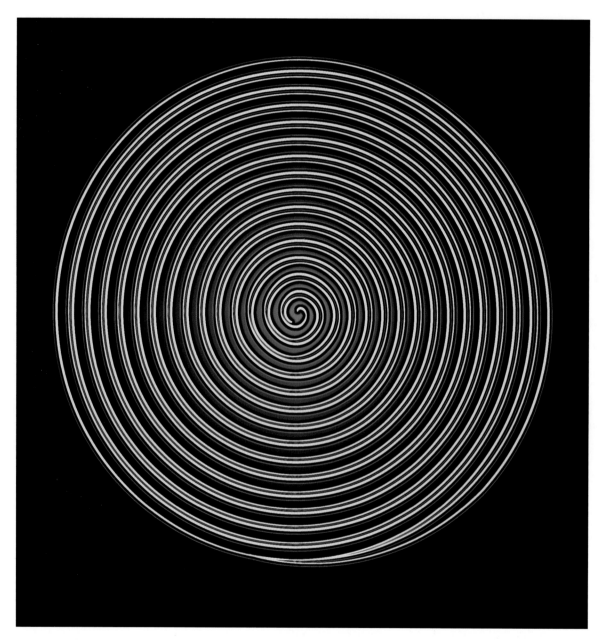

Concentric Circles

Concentrate on the upper part of the disc; can you determine if it
contains concentric circles or just a spiral? Is the disc perfectly circular?

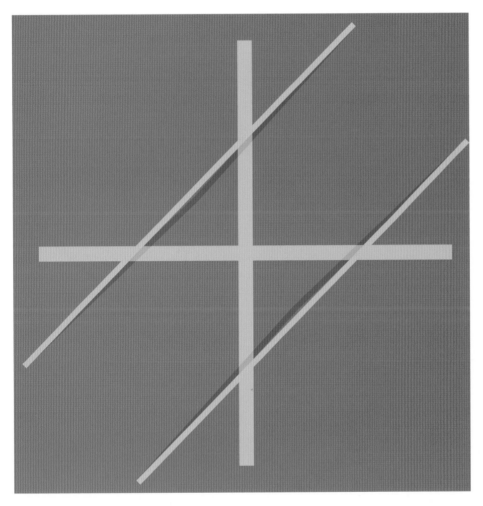

Parallel or Not?
Are the yellow lines bulging outwards?

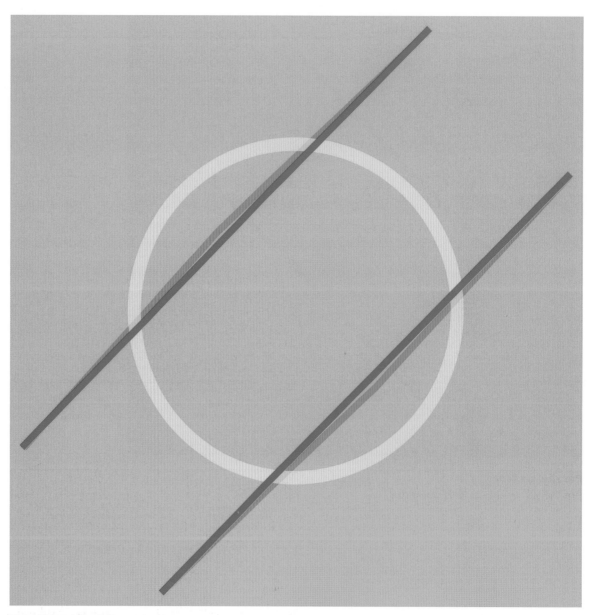

Parallel or Not? 2

Are the green lines straight and parallel to each other?

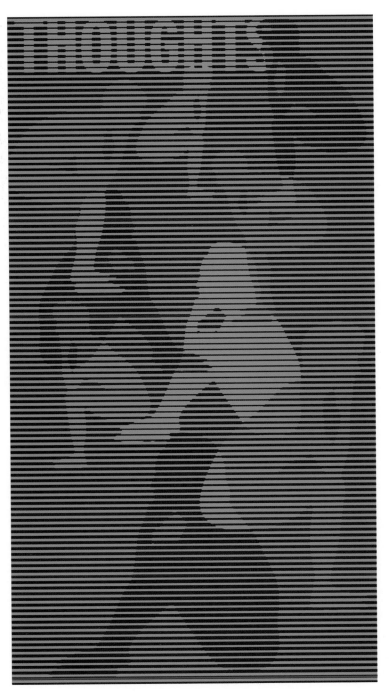

Floating Thoughts
Do you see the shapes of floating thinking men and women? It's just your imagination...

The Mailman's Anguish
What does every mailman fear?

Very, Very Ugly Dog
Find a cute cat in the ugly dog!

Gallery II Notes

Page 50
The three 4s on the right are slightly larger, while the 8s are all the same thickness. The second set of 8s on the right was just turned upside-down.

Page 51
Reassembling puzzles which include triangular pieces may lead to paradoxical conclusions! In this particular case, we have two paradoxes in one when both triangular pieces of the puzzle are inverted:
1. a substantial portion of the puzzle seems to be missing;
2. an egg has vanished.
Of course, apparent gain or loss of area is offset by a complementary loss or gain elsewhere in the puzzle. The loss of the small surface is due to the fact that the bases of the triangles aren't perfectly aligned to form a continuous straight line at the bottom of the puzzle. In figure A, the point where the triangles meet is slightly retracted, whereas in B it is protruding. The area of the 'missing' surface in B is simply redistributed within this prominent line. And what about the missing egg? This is a Columbus egg. By switching the triangular pieces of the puzzle, the egg doesn't disappear at all – a fraction of the image is redistributed among the seven eggs that remain. Can you see that the seven remaining eggs in B are slightly longer than the eight eggs shown in A?
This puzzle, involving the vanishing of a surface as well as the vanishing of a graphic element, is an original novelty invented by the mathemagician Gianni A. Sarcone. You may have heard of him somewhere!

Page 53
Tracing a drawing with the help of a mirror can be very confusing for our procedural memory. The procedural memory is our motion memory. When performing something with procedural memory, one is not consciously aware of exactly how one is performing each individual movement or how to combine the movements. Becoming aware of these things can disrupt a well-learned skill. Now, when you try to draw something by looking in a mirror, you have to inhibit and reverse all that is associated with vision and motion control (and as you have experienced yourself, the first time it is very, very difficult!).

Page 54
Just turn the image upside-down and you will discover a toucan.

Page 55
You can see the presence of five faces in the tails of the cats.

Page 56
The green segments aren't properly aligned to form a straight continuous line.

Page 57
The lines are all the same length. This is a Müller-Lyer illusion variant.

Page 58
In A the vertical slices are different from the horizontal slices.

Pages 59–60
This trick is simply based on visual memory. Hint: people concentrate on the selected card but not on the surrounding playing cards.

Page 61
This is an original after-effect experiment.

Page 62
The disc contains just a spiral and isn't circular at all.

Page 63
No; they are perfectly straight and parallel to each other. This distortion illusion is induced by the cross in the background.

Page 64
Even though they seem to bulge inwards, they are perfectly straight and parallel to each other. This distortion illusion is induced by the circle in the background.

Page 65
There are no really determined shapes in the drawing; just lines and illusory figures!

Page 66
A dog! Find it in the bush at the bottom of the illustration.

Page 67
To find it, just rotate the image counterclockwise by a quarter-turn.

his popular collection of illusions, *Pseudoptics*. The twisted cord effect is probably due to orientation-sensitive simple cells in the striate cerebral cortex, which interact to combine a set of small closely-spaced tilted lines into one single tilted line.

Page 65
You can see her from behind, or if you hide the shaded arm with a pencil (or any other oblong object) you will see her face-on.

Gallery III

Good Vibrations
Do you see
some converging
vibrating flows?
No, you aren't
seeing things;
it's just a natural
lateral inhibition
effect.

The Lonely Dancers
Are they really lonely?

Impossible Eight-Point Star?

Cut slits in two single square paper sheets so that, when the sheets are interlaced, they form this eight-pointed star figure.

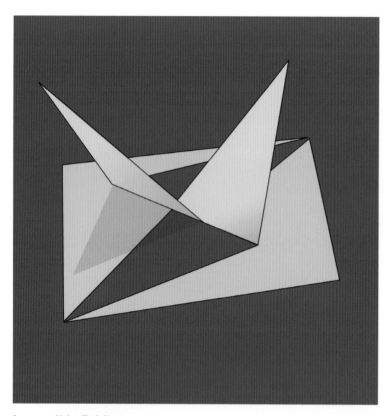

Impossible Foldings

Are you able to reproduce this tri-dimensional figure just by cutting and folding a single piece of strong paper?

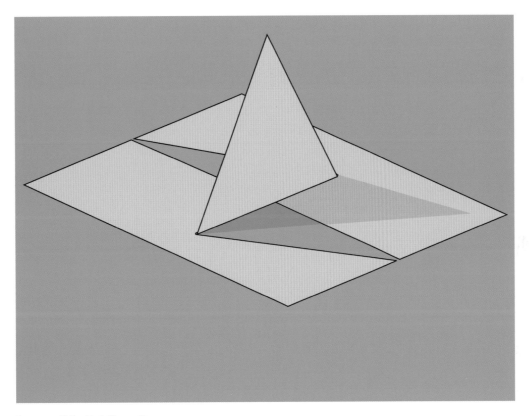

Impossible Foldings 2

Can you reproduce this pyramid-like figure just by cutting and folding a single piece of strong paper? (You cannot cut the paper into two or more different pieces.)

Impossible Stairs 3

Living Eyes
Wherever you are, this face seems to follow you with its eyes.

Gray Gradations

Color gradations can affect the alignment of regular objects. In the picture, the squares are perfectly aligned and parallel!

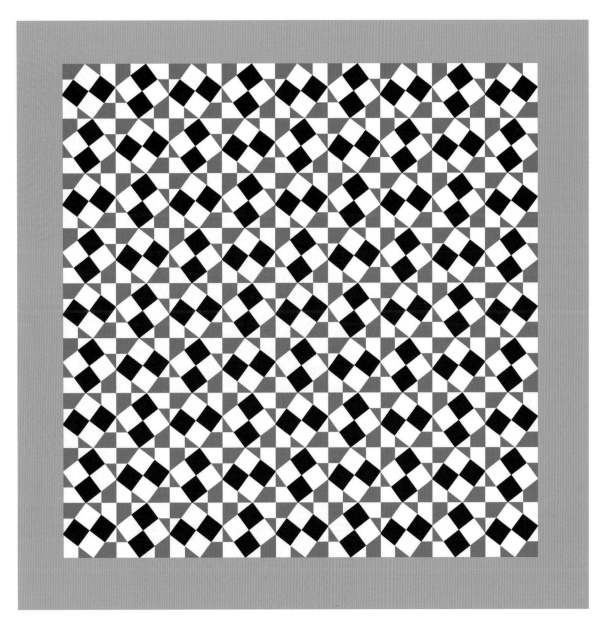

Round Corners?

The checkered small squares seem to have wobbly, round corners.
Squares tend to lose their evenness when assembled in regular sets.

Boing Visual Patterns

An interesting visual effect of coaxial circles and ellipses is created by placing a negative arrangement of concentric black and white circles with an 'invert blending mode' on an alignment of black and white stripes. Changing the thickness of the stripes in the background alters the image dramatically, as illustrated in the three examples.

Make a Magic Cardboard Ball

Take three circular mats or pieces of stiff card and try to assemble them as shown in the picture. The figure is made by cutting and interlocking three single pieces together without glue or adhesive of any kind. Is this figure possible?

Moving Concentric Pattern
Concentric regular arrangements cause visual perturbations.
The picture seems to vibrate.

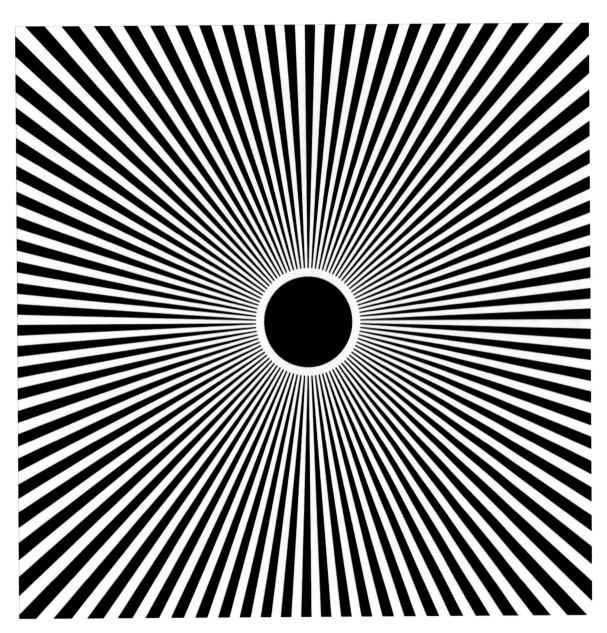

Moving Radial Pattern

Radial patterns can induce visual perturbations. The image seems to shimmer when the page is moved slightly. If you move your eyes around the spokes you may even see color appear.

Magic Top
Move the picture from side to side to make the top spin.

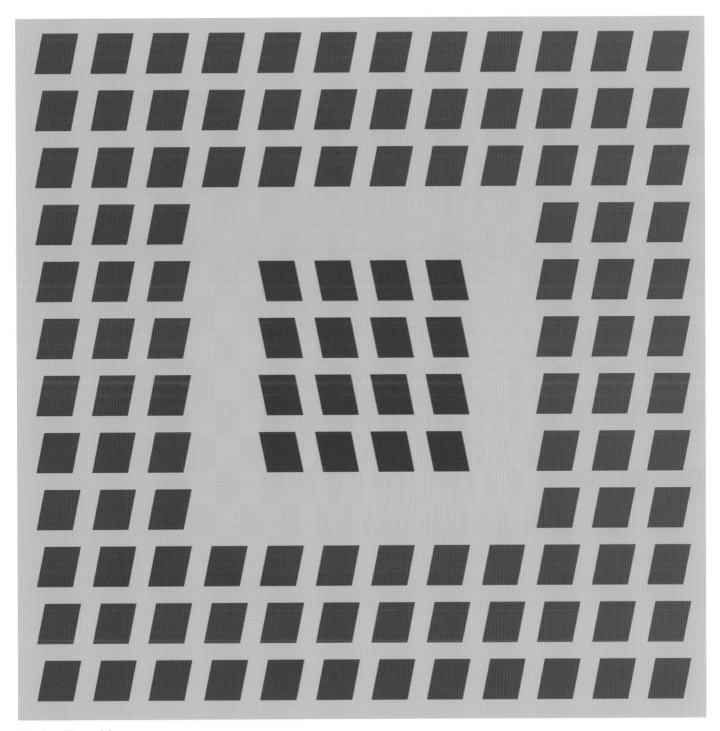

Moving Rhombi

If you shake the image slightly, the inset of blue rhombi starts moving independently of the background and the surrounding orange rhombi.

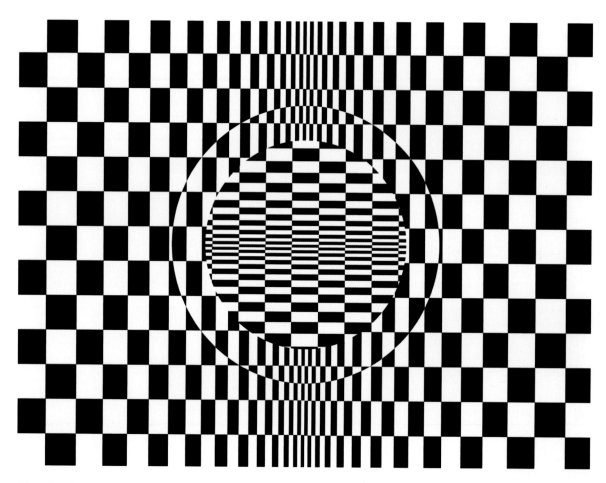

Floating Disc

Observe the image and concentrate on the central disc, while shaking the image slightly. The circular shape appears to separate from the rest of the picture and levitate above the checkered background.

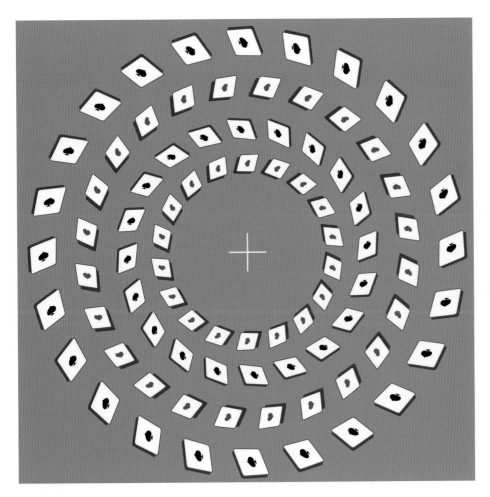

Rotating Circles

The circular sets of playing cards seem to counter-rotate when you move your head backwards and forwards, keeping your focus on the cross in the center of the image. Do you notice something odd?

Horizontal Fluids

Do the curved lines seem to vibrate and blink forwards and backwards?

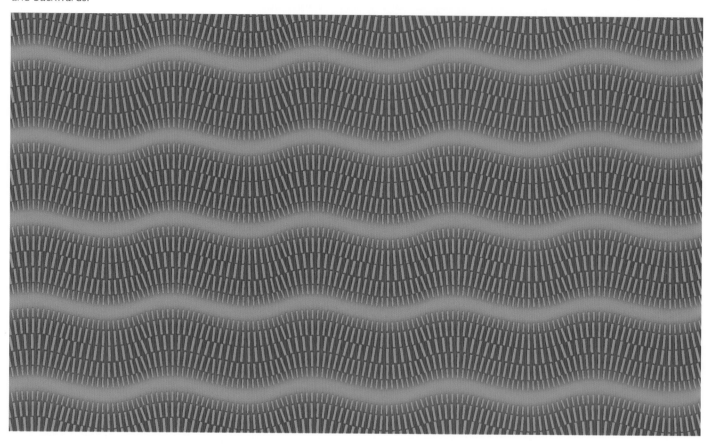

Fill the Van

Is it possible to fit all these boxes into the
van? If not, which pieces cannot be included?

Magic Magic Square

Magic squares are squares filled in by aligned numbers with the characteristic that the sum of the numbers of each row, column, and diagonal is the same. The square featured on this page is a magic magic square. Why?

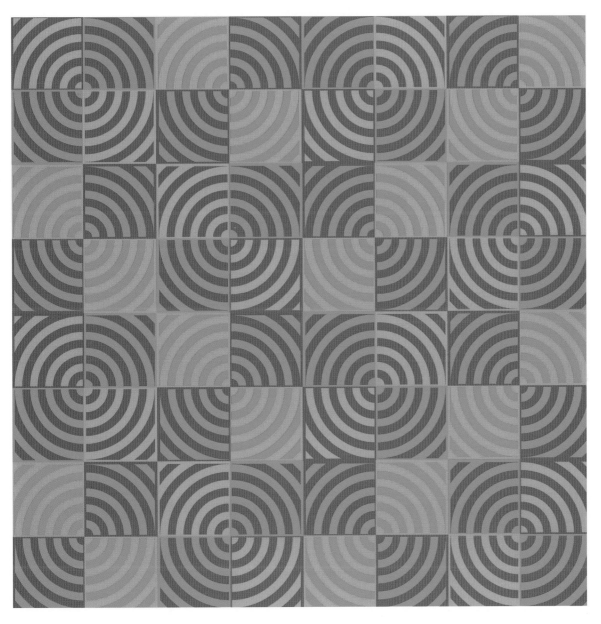

Color Patchwork

Move two meters (six feet) away from this picture and you will see two apparent colors: blue and yellow. But if you observe them closely, you will notice that they are actually orange and green!

Gallery III Notes

Page 72
A woman's face can be perceived at the center of the illustration. This is an ambiguous figure-ground illusion.

Page 73

Here you can see the cuts in the paper sheets which allow you to form an eight-pointed star.

Page 74

Page 75

Page 77

The effect is due to the ambiguity of the face. In fact, we have modified a real unidirectional face (A) by inverting symmetrically the top of the face around a vertical axis. The result (B) is a bidirectional ambiguous face. Our judgment of where a person is fixing his gaze is influenced by set. In this particular case there are two possible sets; in just one image.

Page 81

Here is the secret: cut as shown in the example before you interlock them.

Page 84

Illusory motion is induced by the visual contrasts of the top and its background.

Page 85

We tend to perceive the inset and the surround of rhombi as two independent fields even though they are on the same plane. The surrounding rhombi are interpreted as a 'frame of reference' and tend to be stationary. The visual contrasts of the inset and the surroundings in the picture seem to confuse the motion detector of our visual system.

Page 86

This is a variant of the Ouchi illusion. When you make eye movements while following the picture, the visual contrast of the foreground and background patterns may induce illusory motion at the edges of the central disc. This kind of illusion is thought to arise from retinal motion signals (the motion detector of our visual system). Another interesting observation: the boundaries of the ring which include the Ouchi disc appear to shine slightly, like a neon.

Page 87

The circular set of playing cards with the ace of hearts rotates faster than the circular set with the ace of clubs.

Page 88

Yes, but it is just an illusion induced by the alternating of small light and dark strokes. It is a kind of after-image effect caused by the lateral inhibition of our retina.

Page 89

Yes, the van can contain all the boxes.

Page 90

It is reversible. It remains a magic square even if you turn it upside-down! And if you look at it from a certain distance, the corners of the small orange squares (containing the numbers) lose their regularity and seem to sharpen.

Page 91

It is no secret, and painters have known for centuries, that colors tend to influence each other. Here, two effects are responsible for the apparition of the colors flesh-pink and blue: contrast of color and assimilation of color.

Gallery IV

Aligned Dots?

It seems incredible, but all the dots are the same shade of pink and the dots that appear clearer are perfectly aligned with those which appear darker. Take a ruler and verify the situation for yourself! These illusions are induced by two factors: contrast of colors and the bended colored lines.

A

B
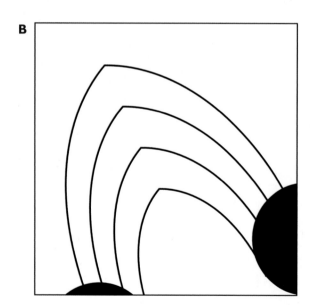

Droodles
What do images A and B represent?

3D Sundial

This picture of a sundial seems confused and flat. Close one eye and look along the direction indicated by the blue triangle at the bottom of the illustration, leaning the book back as you look. What happens?

Shade Effects

Shade may induce objects, like the parallel slats here, to bulge.

COCK

Self-Referring Word

This image represents a self-referential word (the word 'clock' with a clock inside). A self-referential graphic word is a word that encapsulates the thing it represents within itself, like: ei8ht, dOt, lllree, fl rst, para//e/... Can you determine why *semordnilap* is a self-referential word?

Impossible Figure Tiles
With the parallelogram tile, it is possible to assemble an impossible structure.

Triangularize It
Using these three 'blocks', form the
representation of a pyramid.

Impossible Stairs 4

Dead Man?
Do you see the ghost of a dead man?

Bidimensional Temple

Observe the scene: there are several architectural absurdities!

Visual Memory Test 2
Trick question: can you remember which
Roman symbols represent four on
most tower clock dials?

Celestial Shrines

Which shrine is taller: A or B?

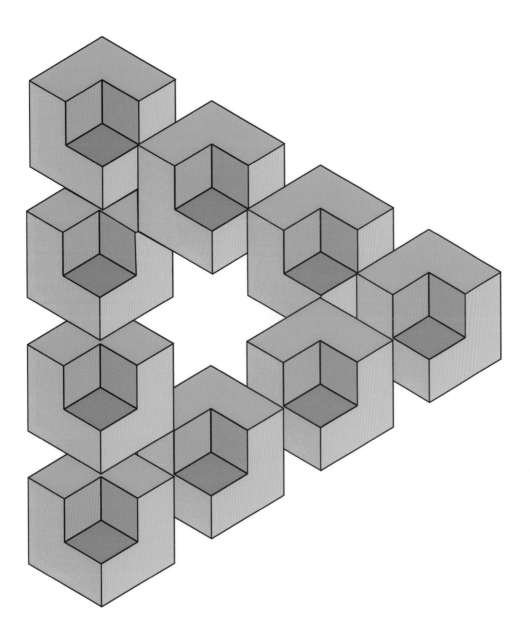

Cubic Tribar

In this impossible figure, called a tribar, do you see two sets of cubes
or just one set of cubes with a small cube cut out?

Blues

The blue spots set on the darker background appear lighter than the blue spots on the clearer background. But all the blue spots have identical hues! This compelling visual phenomenon is described as simultaneous lightness contrast.

Braids of Shade

Three intriguing variants of simultaneous lightness contrast involving lenticular colored shapes (you can see at the bottom of the illustration how the lenticular colored shapes really appear). The two upper examples combine multiple color boundaries and lead to a strong illusion.

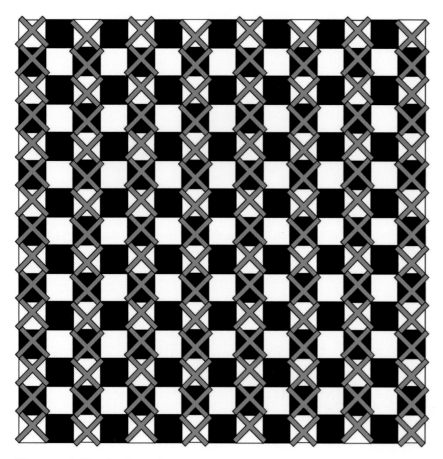

Distorted Checkerboard

Alternating cross patterns make the columns of the checkerboard diverge.

Find the Hidden Shape
Can you find the square in the triangle with your naked eye?

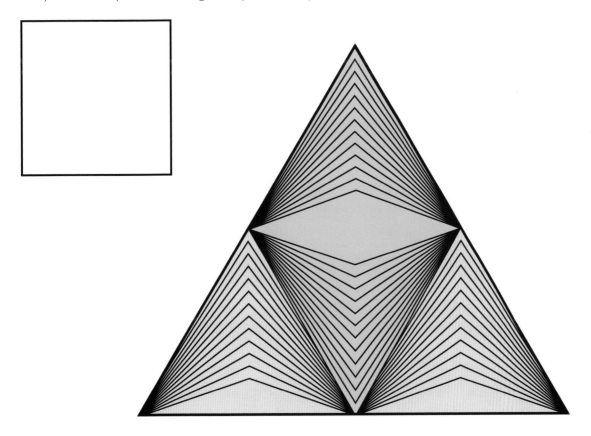

In Common

What do the wrought-iron gates have in common?

Old Trans-Siberian

Reproduce the card depicting an old Trans-Siberian train and cut it into three pieces. Then rearrange the rectangular card again in order to transform this seven-carriage train into a six-carriage one.

Slashed Telescope

The telescope shown in figure A is split by an axe into two pieces (figure B).
Explain why it still works and why it is possible to see through the axe.
(Hint: the axe is not transparent! It is just a question of reflections.)

A Midsummer Day's Dream
Just enjoy this picture which contains this absurdity.

Gallery IV Notes

Page 96
Droodle A is a trombone player doing some stretching exercises before a performance. Droodle B is part of a spider's legs while it stands on a mirror.

Page 97
You will soon notice that the upright stick in the center of the sundial (the pointer) rises (and shrinks in height) all by itself.

Page 99
As *semordnilap* is 'palindromes' written backwards, it's a self-referential word!

Page 101

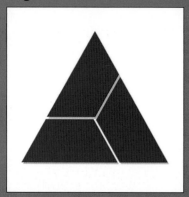

Page 103
It was a joke... 'Dead man' is a little-used British expression for an empty liquor or wine bottle. You will, of course, have noticed a ghostly translucent wine bottle in the picture, but its outline is only determined by the five glasses! The white background within the outline seems slightly yellowish, but in reality it is uniformly white.

Page 105
On most clock dials you may find the Roman figures IIII for 4, instead of IV. Here is another curiosity about dials. Tell a friend that you are able to guess the position of the hands of any watch featured in a magazine or a review. Then ask him to browse a magazine of his choice and to concentrate on the first advertisement representing a watch he may find. The minute and hour hands will most probably point to 10 past 10. These experiments are based on peculiar traditions and customs which pass unobserved by most people.

Page 106
Our intuition about perspective strongly influences what we see.

Though shrine B appears larger, both shrines are actually the same height. This is a variation of the Ponzo illusion.

Page 107
The illusion combines two illusions in one: an impossible figure together with an ambiguous figure.

Page 108
The observation that a color looks darker when set against white than when set against black has puzzled scientists and philosophers for two millennia, yet there is still no consensus as to exactly why it happens. Interesting observations and comments on this subject are provided by scientists Edward Adelson (lightness induction) and Alexander Logvinenko (lightness-shadow invariance).

Page 109
All the lenticular colored shapes are of the same shade, but we see lighter and darker lenticular shapes. We encounter a similar effect in everyday life: the screen of the television and of the PC aren't black at all, nor can black be created by the electron beams. But when you switch on your television you can see all the colors, black included!

Page 110
All the columns are perfectly parallel and aligned. This illusion is related to the Zöllner illusion.

Page 111

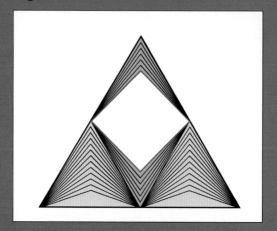

Page 112
Observe the empty spaces... Both gates have the same arrow-shaped empty spaces. When you notice them, you cannot miss them any more because they become insistent in your visual field.

Page 113

The steam train will lose a wagon depending on the way pieces A and B of the puzzle are reassembled.

Page 114

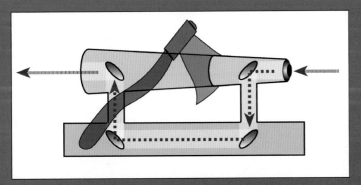

The trick lies in the four mirrors concealed in the telescope's prop.

Gallery V

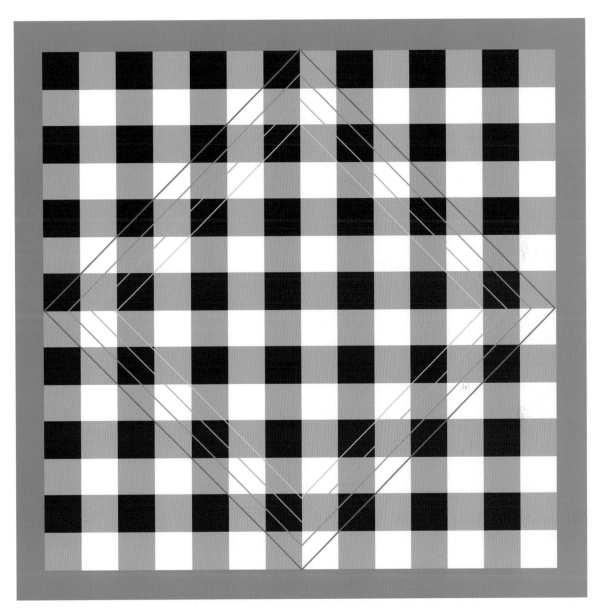

Good Vibrations 2

Are the colors really vibrating? The checkered background induces
the color outlines to vibrate slightly. This is a kind of after-image
effect and is mainly due to lateral inhibition.

Find the Hidden Shape 2
Find the cross in the square!

Find the Hidden Shape 3

Follow your star... Find it in the pattern.

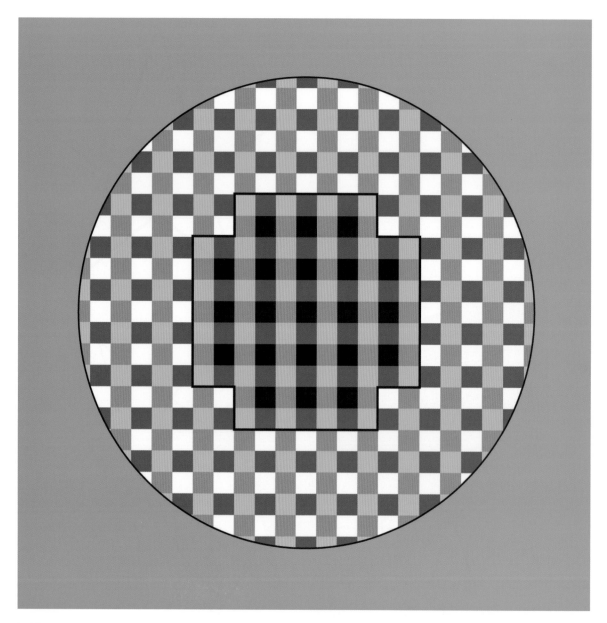

It Floats!

Using only squares, it is possible to create a pattern that evokes an apparent swinging sensation. Move the page slightly to and fro and the inset cross appears to move and 'float' relative to the background circular pattern.

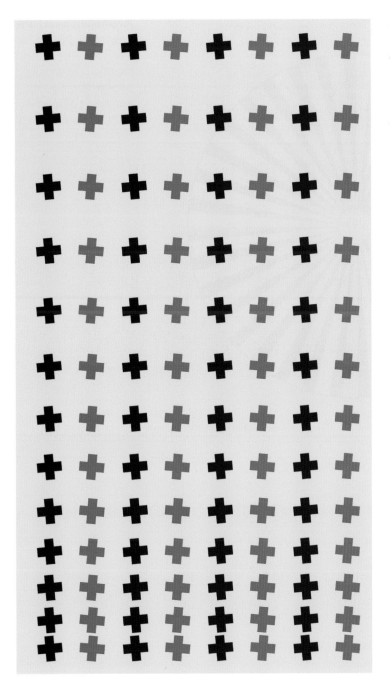

Divergent Crosses
Each pair of columns, made up of black and red crosses, seem to diverge.

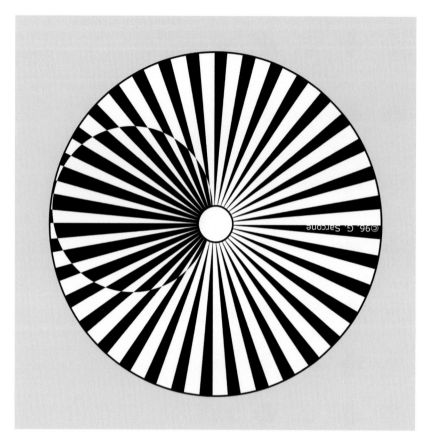

Artificial Spectrum Top

Reproduce this circular pattern and paste it on to a piece of cardboard, then cut out the disc. Push a short, pointed pencil through its center. You now have a top with magic properties. Spin the top and you'll see subjective colors while it rotates.

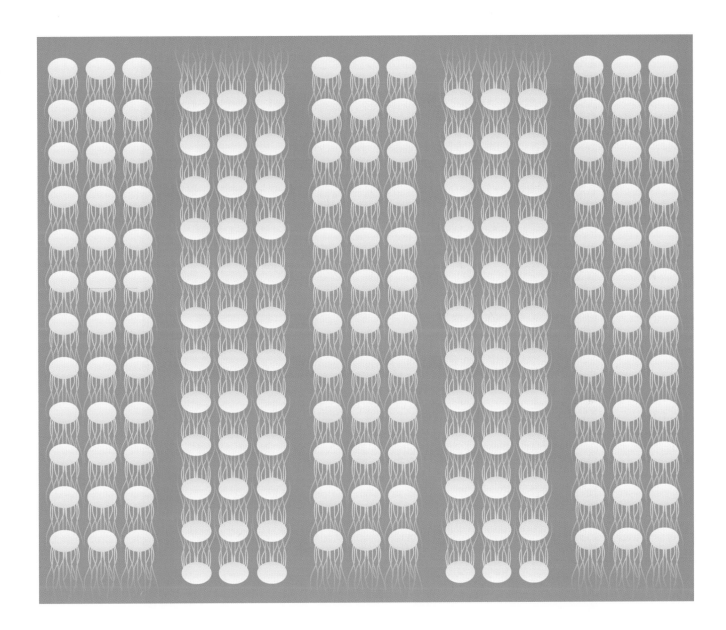

Moving Jellyfish

Stare at the image and imagine that the blue is the sea. Concentrate and cast your eyes around the groups of jellyfish and they will start to move in opposite directions.

Same Hue

The rows of lozenges indicated by the red and green arrows in figures A and B have exactly the same hue!

Concentric or Not?
At a certain distance, the circles, composed of twisted strands of
rope of two different colors, may appear confused and diverging.

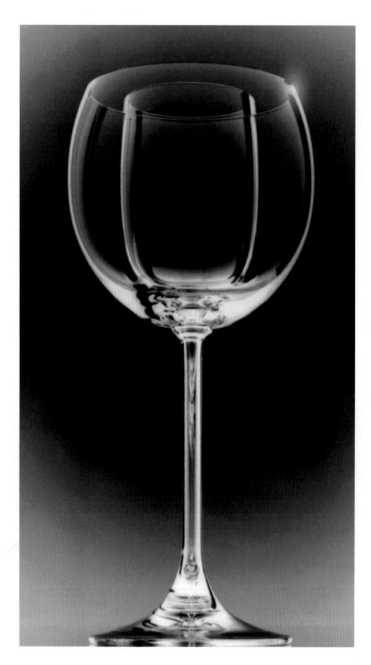

Glass Ambiguity

Do you see two glasses or one glass with a strange double container? If you see two glasses, which one is behind the other?

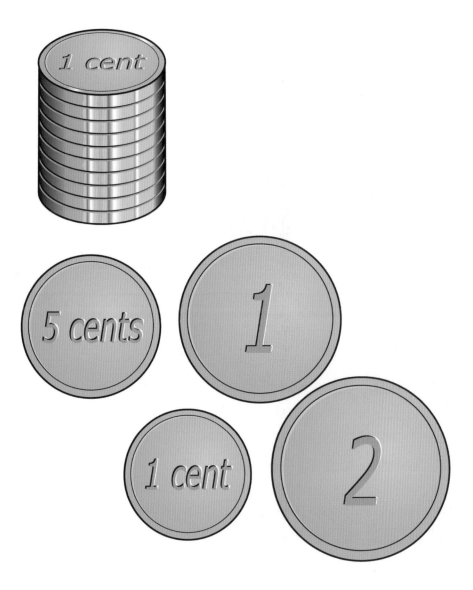

Magic Pile
Which coin, balanced on its edge, exactly matches the height of the stack of one-cent pieces?

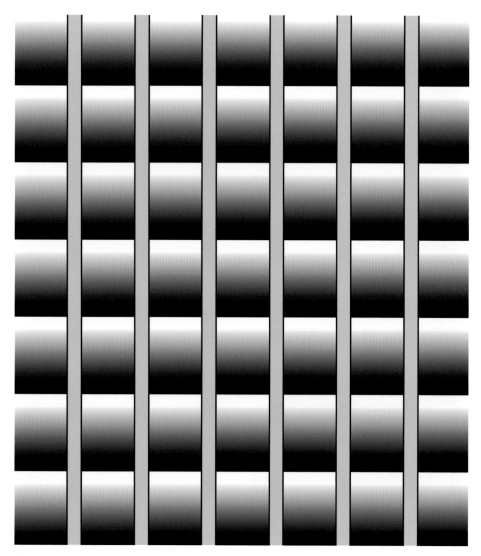

Unreal Bamboos

The dark gray boundaries which segment the 'bamboos' don't actually exist.
The 'bamboos' are perfectly straight and parallel.

Yellow Lines
Are the yellow lines perfectly straight?

Impossible Stairs 5

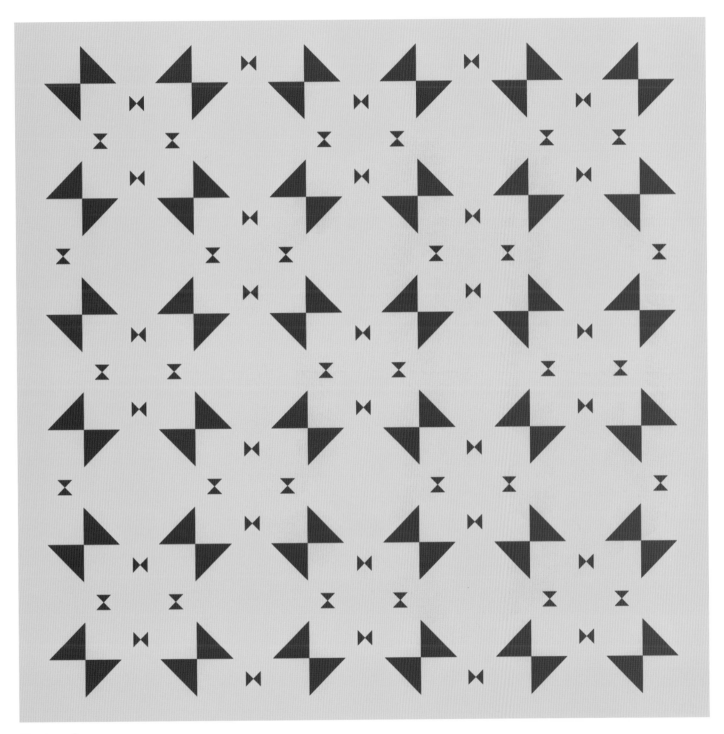

Kanisza Squares

How many perfect squares do you perceive?

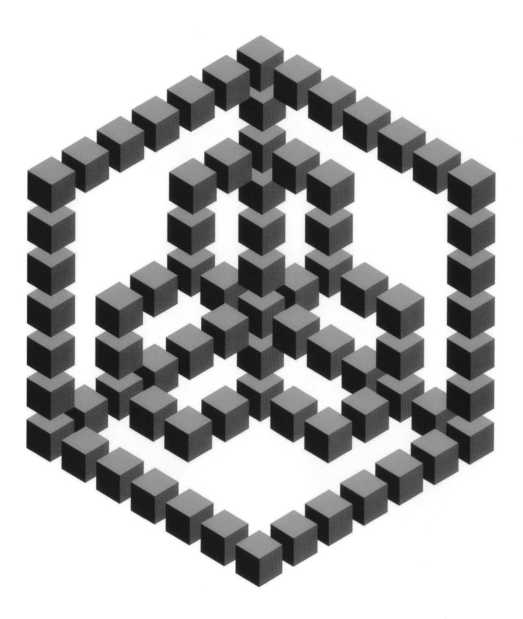

Impossible Cubic Structure

Just a neat cubic 3D structure...

Listeners and Conductors
This is a figure-ground illusion. How many people do you perceive on this page?

Running Water

Do the blue lines twist up and down like a water flow?

Please turn off the faucets once you've experienced the illusion!

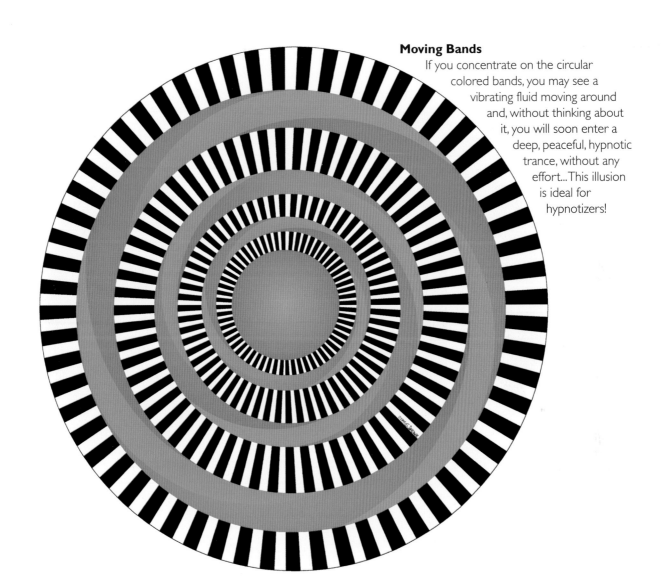

Moving Bands

If you concentrate on the circular colored bands, you may see a vibrating fluid moving around and, without thinking about it, you will soon enter a deep, peaceful, hypnotic trance, without any effort...This illusion is ideal for hypnotizers!

Gallery V Notes

Page 120

Page 121

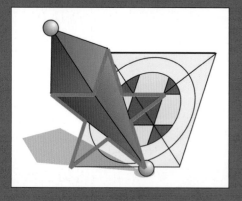

Page 122
We've just replaced the white squares of the background pattern within the cross with black squares, and that is sufficient to induce a sensation of apparent movement. This illusion is related to the Ouchi illusion.

Page 123
This illusion is related to the Zöllner illusion.

Page 124
The 'color' observed with such rotating discs does not exist. If the disc is rotated in one direction 'colors' of red to blue may appear. If the disc is rotated in the other direction, the colors appear in the reverse order. Colors obtained with this top are subjective colors or – using a scientific term – pattern-induced flicker colors. The effect observed depends on the intensity of the light source, the speed of rotation and the design and distribution of the black lines. Observation in bright sunshine gives very satisfactory results.

There isn't a complete and certain explanation concerning the observance of subjective colors.. Lateral inhibition and the different rates of stimulation for the color receptors in the eye are clearly involved.

Page 125
This illusory motion is related to the central drift illusion. The factor that induces this illusion may be the difference in contrast between the inner and outer areas of the 'moving' objects (jellyfish).

Page 126
This is what we call a simultaneous lightness contrast effect. The pattern in A is based on Adelson's tile pattern; the pattern in B is based on Logvinenko's modified tile pattern (in which dark regions of pattern A have been blurred). The effect seems stronger with pattern B.

Page 127
This illusion is also known as the twisted cord illusion. It actually consists of perfectly concentric circles of twisted cords. The visual distortion is produced by combining a regular line pattern (the concentric circles) with misaligned parts (the differently colored strands). The Zöllner and café wall illusions are based on a similar principle, like many other visual effects, in which a sequence of tilted elements causes the eye to perceive phantom twists and deviations.

Page 128
There are actually two glasses. The slender glass is aligned behind the other one.

Page 129

One cent! This experiment demonstrates the difficulty of judging the real size of circular objects. Using real coins, you can demonstrate this trick to your friends.

Page 130
The illusion of dark gray spots is induced by the sinusoidal gratings on the background. This is a classical case of lateral inhibition.

Page 131
The yellow lines are perfectly straight and parallel. Some visual illusions, like this one, occur in interrupted modular patterns.

Page 133

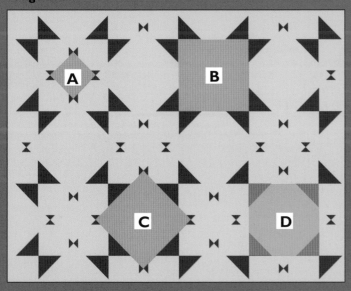

In the picture there are 13 small squares A, 13 squares B, 12 squares C and 12 squares D. In total, there are 50 squares.

Page 134
This impossible structure, called multi-link cubes, was created by Vicente Meavilla Seguí.

Page 135
There are two enigmatic opera listeners (green) and two conductors (yellow).

Page 136
The illusion is due to lateral inhibition.

Page 137
Another lateral inhibition effect.

Gallery VI

The Reader
Who appears to be listening to the reader?

Rubber Ducks

Let's try an experiment with a color filling-in effect. Have a look at these cute rubber ducks from a distance of two meters (six feet). Most people only see yellow inside the outline of the ducks…

Elusive Pencils

Hold two pencils – a blue one and a red one – level in front of you. Focus on them. Slowly bring the tips of the two pencils together. No problems? Try the same thing with just one eye open. Easy? Not the same, is it?

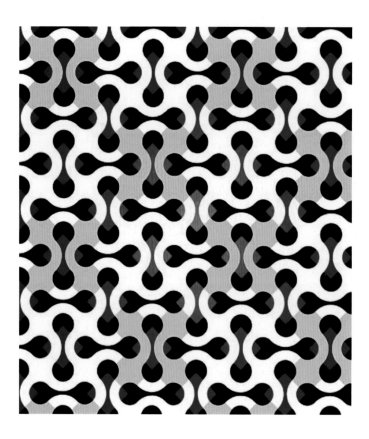

Hypnotic Neon Lights
Do you see a pattern of large and small squares? The seemingly neon squares seem to pulse slightly when you concentrate on the image.

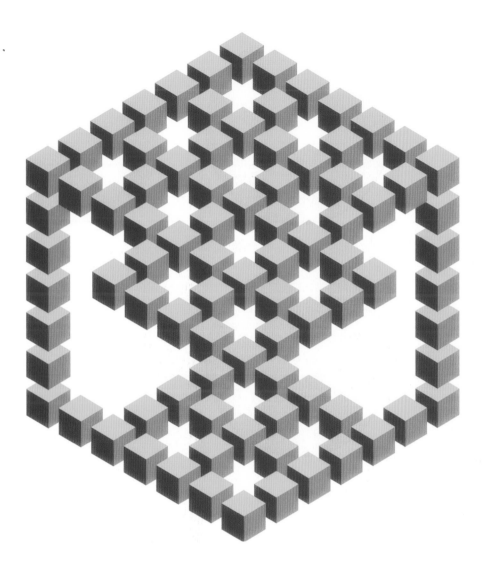

Impossible Cubic Structure 2
This is another curious cubic 3D structure.

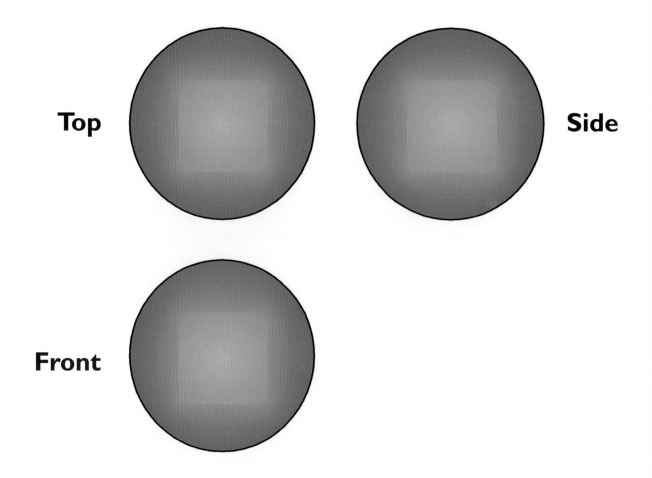

Top

Side

Front

This Is Not a Sphere…
The 3D object above, seen from three different points of view, is
not a sphere. Can you imagine what kind of solid it is?

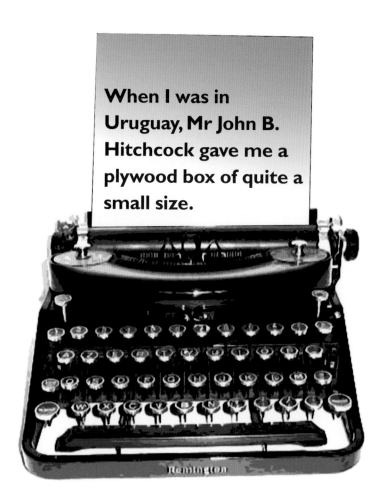

When I was in Uruguay, Mr John B. Hitchcock gave me a plywood box of quite a small size.

Incomplete Keyboard
This is a visual attention test. Does the typed sentence contain all the letters of the alphabet? If not, which one is missing?

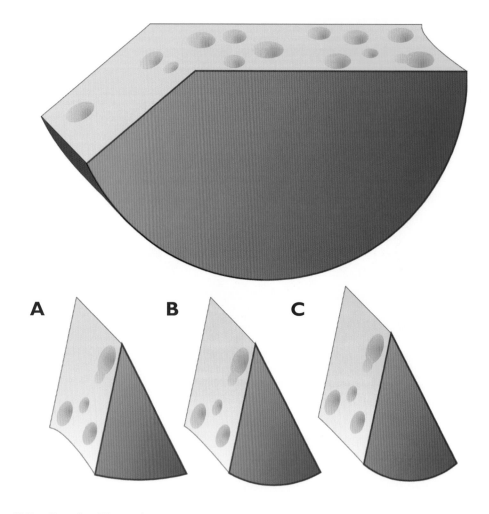

Who Cut the Cheese!
Which piece of cheese is cut from the semicircular Emmenthal cheese?

Mystery House
Find three weird perspective errors in the picture above.

Gallery VI Notes

Page 141

Rotate the page half a turn clockwise and you'll discover the face of a giant.

Page 142

If you closely examine a rubber duck (without squeezing it) you'll notice that it is printed on a yellow rectangle (and the color obviously doesn't fill the exact inner surface of the duck!) Some colors, like yellow, have a low *spatial resolution*. That means it is difficult to perceive and define a determined yellow shape on a clear background. So, our visual system tends to constrain yellow colors in outlines.

Page 143

Each eye sees from a slightly different angle (binocular disparity). Both eyes work together to give us depth perception. You need depth perception for your brain to be able to judge distance. When you only use one eye, you lose depth perception. Depth perception is also dependent on colors; objects with warm colors tend to be seen as nearer than objects with cold colors.

Page 144

I say 'seemingly' neon squares because the wavy pattern gives the impression that there are whole squares lying behind it. But, as the entire design lies on the same plane, the apparently pulsating squares are really just segmented colored shapes. Neon color spreading contains illusory contours, brightness induction, color assimilation, and perceptual transparency, all of which gives depth perception. Neon color spreading can also be observed in the Kanizsa triangle. In fact, Varin first observed it in 1971, but the name 'neon color' came from Van Tuijl. The human ability to perceive a neon effect may be a remnant of the development of our power of sight under water at extreme depths as there is a lack of light there.

Page 145

This impossible structure, called *multi-link cubes,* was created by Vicente Meavilla Seguí.

Page 146

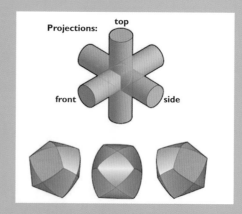

The object, which is the resulting geometry from the perpendicular intersections of three cylinders, is called a *tricylinder* (or *Steinmetz solid*) and has the same top, front and side views as a sphere. Both the sphere and the tricylinder have circles as projection. This proves that a 3D object cannot be uniquely described by a top, front and side view! QED.

Page 147

Actually, the sentence does contain all the letters of the alphabet. Maybe you've answered that the letter 'F' is missing… This is because you couldn't find it in the word 'of'. *Function words* like 'of', 'from' and 'and' are unconsciously processed by your brain because they haven't any specific lexical meaning for the text.

Page 148

We are sure you have answered 'piece of cheese b)', but you'd be wrong! The correct answer is 'piece of cheese a)'.

Page 149

The door is open simultaneously out and in (and that's not the only mystery here…). The roof ends in another direction in relation to the house; and the leaves near the entry steps are ambiguous – we cannot see whether they lie on the ground or on the branches of the trees.

CLASSIC OPTICAL ILLUSIONS

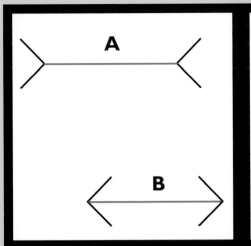

Müller-Lyer Illusion
line a = line b

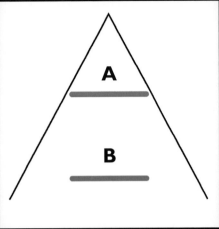

Ponzo Illusion
line a = line b

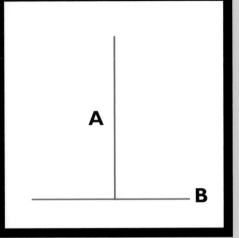

Fick Illusion
line a = line b

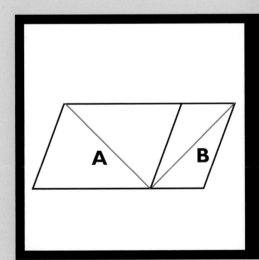

Sander Parallelogram
line a = line b

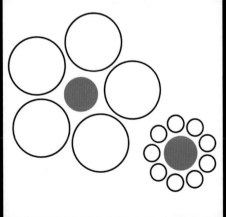

Ebbinghaus Illusion
equal red circles

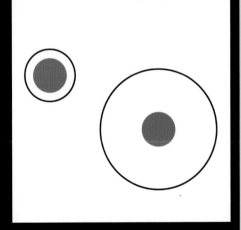

Delboeuf Illusion
equal red circles

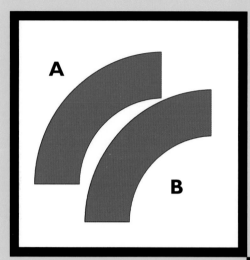

Jastrow Illusion
shape a = shape b

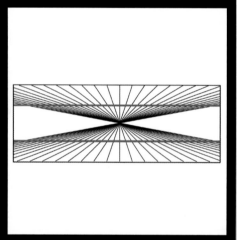

Hering Illusion
red lines are parallel

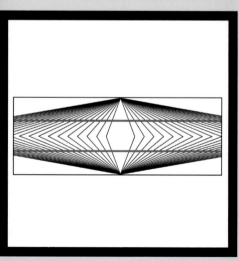

Wundt Illusion
red lines are parallel

Zöllner Illusion
parallel diagonals

Ehrenstein Illusion
perfect square

Orbison Illusion
perfect circle

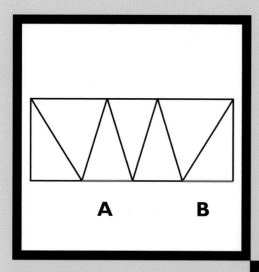

Fee Illusion
line a = line b

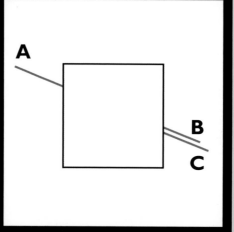

Poggendorff Illusion
segments a and b are aligned

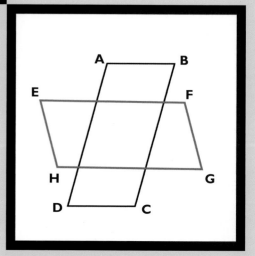

Crossed-parallelogram Illusion
parallelogram ABCD = parallelogram EFGH

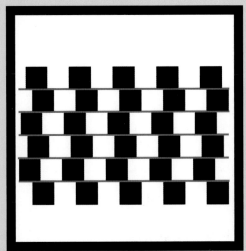

Cafe Wall Illusion
red lines are straight and parallel

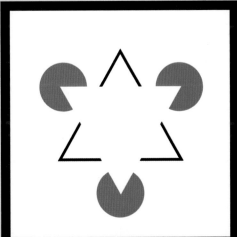

Kanisza Illusion
phenomenal subjective white triangle

Frazer Illusion
lines are parallel

Glossary

Ambigram
A graphic word or sentence that can be read in more than one way. This can be achieved in several ways: by writing the word so that it can be interpreted in more than one way, or by making it meaningful when turned upside-down.

Ambiguous figures
Open to more than one interpretation. It means that an image as a whole can display different scenes, depending on the interpretation of the viewer.

Blind spot
We cannot see where the optical nerve enters our eye. We don't ever notice it because our eyes constantly make small movements and, above all, our mind just fills in the gap. It just guesses what should be there. The blind spot is actually quite big, as you can see by taking the test on page 139 in this book.

Color contrast and color assimilation
Color contrast refers to the change of hue when colors are perceived in the context of other colors. For instance, colors may look lighter or darker with respect to the background color, or even shift their hues into the direction of the complementary background color. When the areas of color in a pattern are very small, an effect opposite to simultaneous color contrast occurs: colors appear to become more like their neighbor instead of less like them.

Entasis
The slight convex curve used on Greek columns. This curve compensates for the optical illusion that a straight column seems concave.

Hidden images and Camouflage
Camouflage has been used for disguise in the natural world ever since predators developed eyes to track prey. In optical illusions, it is the art of hiding something elegantly in an image. Most often these are landscapes or natural scenes where extra animals or objects are hidden.

Impossible images
Impossible figures can be drawn on paper, but can't exist in real life.

Lateral inhibition
Some photoreceptors of the retina are activated when they detect light, while others are activated in the absence of light. These two types usually encircle each other and are spread throughout the retina, creating receptive fields. Often, light can fall onto both light and dark photoreceptors causing the two regions to compete with one another. One part of the receptive field wants to become active while the other part does not. This competitive interaction is called lateral inhibition. Because of this antagonistic nature of receptive fields, perceptual illusions, such as the Herman grid illusion, can occur when we look at certain patterns.

Pareidolia
A kind of illusion or misperception where something meaningless is considered meaningful. For example, recognizing a giraffe in a cloud.

Procrypsis
The ability to blend into the background. This environmental camouflage is most often seen with insects and many animals. Just think of walking sticks and those weird bugs that look like leaves.

Upside-down images
An upside-down or topsy turvy image is an image showing something meaningful when turned around. That can be one thing, or something completely different.

Recent works by the same authors
Almanach du Mathématicien en Herbe, Sarcone & Wäber, Edition Archimède, Paris, 2002
Matemagica, Sarcone & Wäber, La Meridiana Editore, Italy, 2005

Some resourceful and richly illustrated books
Visual Games, Franco Agostini, 1980 (unique!)
Can You Believe Your Eyes?, J. Block & H. Yuker, Mazel Publisher, 1992
The Playful Eye, Mel Gooding, Redstone Press, 1999
Adventures with Impossible Objects, Bruno Ernst, Evergreen Editor, 2002.

Original and interesting sites on optical illusions
http://www.archimedes-lab.org/index_optical.html
  (Archimedes' Lab's perceptual illusion site)
http://www.michaelbach.de/ot/ (optical illusions by a specialist)
http://www.ritsumei.ac.jp/~akitaoka/index-e.html
  (A. Kitaoka's optical illusion site)
http://members.lycos.co.uk/brisray/optill/vision3.htm
  (Perceptual Science Group, MIT)
http://web.mit.edu/persci/people/adelson/illusions_demos.html
  (E. Adelson's optical illusion site)
http://members.lycos.nl/amazingart/E/index.html (amazing art site)
http://www.planetperplex.com/en/optical_illusions.html
  (perplexing illusions)

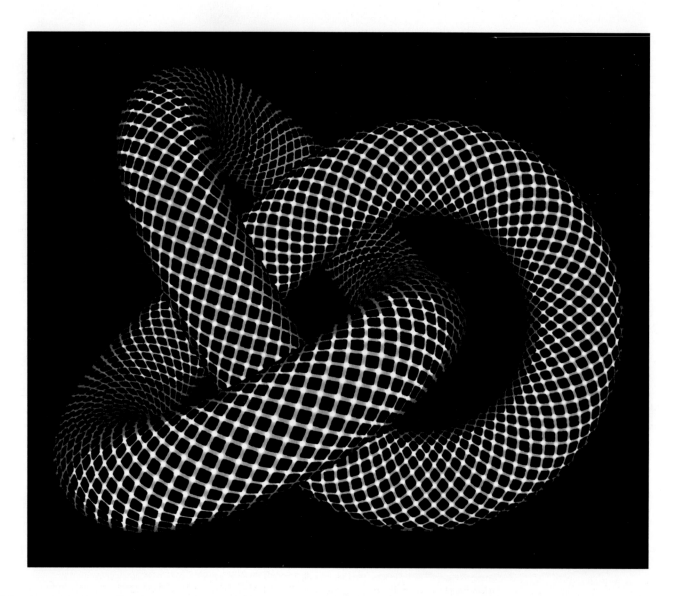

Picture credits

The authors would like to acknowledge the following sources. Any oversights, omissions or corrections will be updated in future editions of this work.

Page 86: Floating Disc inspired by a design of Hajime Ouchi.
Page 109: Braids of Shade inspired by a design of E. Adelson (criss-cross illusion).
Page 126: Same Hue based on A. Logvinenko and E. Adelson tile patterns.
Pages 134 and 145: Impossible Cubic Structures based on a drawing by V. Meavilla Seguí.

Further reading

New Optical Illusions, Sarcone & Waeber, Carlton Books, London, 2005

MateMagica, Sarcone & Waeber, Edizioni La Meridiana, Italy, 2005

Almanach du mathématicien en herbe, Sarcone, Edition Archimède, Paris, 2002